The Haunted Moustache began life as a one-man show, winning awards for 'Best Comedy' and 'Outstanding Theatre' during Brighton Fringe Festival. It was adapted for BBC Radio 3 and won a Sony Silver Award for 'Best Feature.' David Bramwell is the author of *The No9 Bus to Utopia*, singer-songwriter in Oddfellow's Casino and host of Brighton's Catalyst Club. He is a medical man by rumour only.

DRBRAMWELL.COM   @DRBRAMWELL

Dedicated to the memory
of Great Aunt Sylvia,
Adrian Bunting, Marty and
Drako Zarhazar. And to the
incorrigible spirit of Brighton.

Everything in this book is true.
At least, that's how I'd like to
remember it.

THE HAUNTED MOUSTACHE

NIGHTFINCH BOOKS

First published 2016 by Nightfinch Books, Europa House,
Goldstone Villas, Hove, East Sussex BN3 3RQ
www.nightfinch.co.uk
ISBN 9780956130334

Photo credits:
p11-12 © Woodhall Spa Cottage Museum
p15 © The Kinema in the Woods
p35 © Royal Pavilion and Brighton Museums
p61 © National Media Museum/Science & Society Picture Library
p73 © Martineau and Woodhall Spa Cottage Museum
p99 all efforts have been made to trace the owner of this image
p115 © Royal Pavilion and Brighton Museums
p118 and 129 all efforts have been made to trace the owners of these images
p135 Max Ernst © Tate Modern/DACS.org.uk
p139 Dali © CSG CIC Glasgow Museums Collection
p154 © Neel Morley
p173 all efforts have been made to trace the owner of this image
pp179 and 188 © Toby Amies

Edited by Tim Bick and Sadie Mayne
Art direction by David Bramwell and Tim Bick
Cover design by Cristiana Couceiro

CONTENTS

CHAPTER ONE   It Starts With A Death   P6

CHAPTER TWO   A Cabaret Of Misfits   P30

CHAPTER THREE   Enter The Spirit World   P50

CHAPTER FOUR   Yellow-bellied Wonderland   P66

CHAPTER FIVE   The World's Smallest Theatre   P84

CHAPTER SIX   The Somnambulist   P100

CHAPTER SEVEN   The Gnostic Cult   P112

CHAPTER EIGHT   Marty's Lecture   P130

CHAPTER NINE   The Man With No Memory   P146

CHAPTER TEN   Oddfellow's Hand   P156

CHAPTER ELEVEN   It Ends With A Death   P176

CHAPTER TWELVE   Epilogue   P182

ONE

In which a singular
inheritance is bequeathed
and we learn a thing or two
about opium, organs
and Doncaster.

IT STARTS WITH A DEATH

In the early summer of 1991 my Great Aunt Sylvia sailed out of this world, fag in hand, leaving behind an unfinished jigsaw of the Eiffel Tower and a doleful cat. She made it to the over-ripe age of 96 before death consumed her, leaving a cold, brittle frame curled up by the kitchen table. Sylvia had pottered her way through two world wars, four monarchs and twenty-three prime ministers.

'But what did she ever do with her life?' a heartless relative once remarked.

For almost a century Sylvia lived in the Lincolnshire village of Woodhall Spa, an oasis amid the empty farmland and quiet villages that dominate this flat, damp county. Woodhall had been just another sleepy hamlet until 1811, when entrepreneur John Parkinson bought 400 acres of land nearby and began digging for coal. He pumped his life savings into the project, hoping that the deep mine-shafts would bring great riches. They didn't. Plagued by serious and prolonged water-logging of the excavations, Parkinson eventually abandoned the mine. Broken and bankrupted he soon took to drink.

Great Aunt Sylvia

A few months later a miracle occurred, after two of Woodhall's residents witnessed a lame horse drinking the water from Parkinson's flooded mine. It walked away cured. A sample of the water was analysed and found to contain high percentages of bromide and iodine, leading to great excitement in the village. Woodhall's future as a spa town was set, and in 1830 its Spa Baths and Pump Room were opened to the public. The local paper, *The Horncastle News*, proclaimed:

> "We believe there is a great future in store for the Spa. The upper classes are beginning to realise that when in search of health they can obtain what they need in Lincolnshire and need not journey to the land of sauerkraut and Teutonic rapidity."

Woodhall proved to be a healthy rival to the far-flung spa towns of Europe, with visitors arriving by the trainload. Bathing in and drinking its mineral-rich waters were considered a cure-all for scrofula, glandular problems, rheumatism, gout and a whole host of other maladies. One news report told of an infirm, elderly gentleman who was carried to Woodhall by three strong men and, after a week of baths and drink cures, "got up and danced his way home." But the waters didn't always work their magic. Despite three weeks of intense treatment and twenty-four-hour supervision, one tortured soul took his life by launching himself head-first off the roof of the Pump Room into the dirt road below. It was John Parkinson.

By the early 1900s, visitors to Woodhall were not limited merely to those in search of a cure for their ailments. With a growing reputation as a bohemian outpost, the village began to attract the dandies, spiritualists, table-tappers and followers of

The Spa Baths and Pump Room c.1920

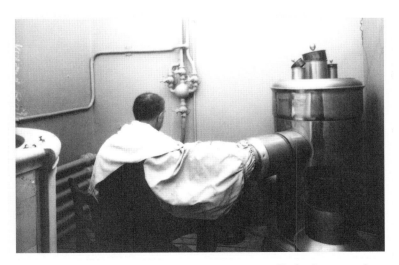

Hydrotherapy at the spa

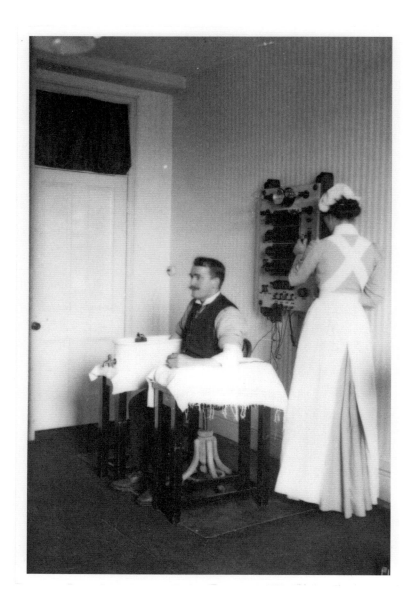

the great Russian mystics, Madame Blavatsky and G.I. Gurdjieff. Woodhall even acquired a royal celebrity, Lady Weigall, who built the Petwood Estate and threw extravagant parties, surrounding herself with artists, clairvoyants and eccentrics. Among Lady Weigall's notorious in-crowd was the celebrated prankster Mr P. Webster, who once survived a descent down Niagara Falls thanks to a ridiculous cork suit he had invented. Another was author Theodore Thomas, who spent much of his time hanging around music concerts in a state of drunken stupor. Thomas achieved minor celebrity status after writing a book on the "curious effects of instrumental music." In it Thomas noted: "when Wagner is played, five times as much beer is sold," "champagne flows freely with Strauss" while "on Mendelssohn nights, hardly anyone wants ham sandwiches." Most eccentric of all was Ambrose Oddfellow, the moustachioed host of a resident freakshow, whom Lady Weigall paid to entertain her guests with theatrical séances. Woodhall was, for a time, Lincolnshire's answer to Glastonbury.

After the Second World War, the fortunes of the village turned again. By the Seventies the spa was in a state of decay and in 1983 it bathed its last customer. While Woodhall has long since surrendered its bohemian reputation to an army of retired RAF officers and golfing fanatics, its pre-war charm and eccentricity lives on through the Kinema In The Woods. Nestled in ancient woodland this enchanted cinema serves up the movies on a silver salver. Entering the Kinema is a magic carpet ride back to the golden era of film where, halfway through the main feature, the Mighty Compton organ still rises from the bowels of the stage, to be played by a man in bottle glasses and florid knitwear.

It is Great Aunt Sylvia I have to thank for some glorious childhood memories of the Kinema: walking through the dappled light of the woodland trail from her pebbledash council house to this magical old pavilion, where we would sit in the gloom, overdosing on boiled sweets and fizzy pop, goggle-eyed at the latest Bond or Disney epic. Sylvia seemed at her happiest here too, lost in the drama and a fug of cigarette smoke. The building seemed to hold some mysterious power over her, like a roguish ex-lover for whom she still carried a torch.

The youngest of five siblings, Sylvia never married. She was a taciturn soul, engrossed in her own private world. Our family visits were partly prompted by a sense of duty. My parents would often arrive armed with books and magazines and the three of them would sit reading in silence while I roamed the garden and fields in search of adventure. I looked forward to these trips; Sylvia always treated me with great kindness, plying me with stacks of cigarette and tea cards, which I collected with zeal.

My great aunt played the part of the professional spinster to perfection. She kept cats, consumed tea by the bucket-load, knitted for England and always had a jigsaw on the go. Like so many of Woodhall's older residents, she also dabbled in spiritualism. Books on divination, psychic healing and the afterlife littered her cramped living room shelves and tables. Such beliefs were not shared by my parents. Once when I was ten, Sylvia's offer to read my future with her tarot cards had met with such vehement disapproval from my dad that it was never suggested again.

Her sole vice was nicotine; a lifelong forty-a-day habit had turned her teeth and skin the colour of mustard. The cigarette was

SOUND ENTERTAINMENT.

Clear and Distinct TALKIES,

Pleasant to the Ear.

Mondays, Tuesdays, Thursdays and Fridays at 7-45 p.m.

Wednesdays and Saturdays at 6 and 8 p.m.

The unique setting of "THE KINEMA IN THE WOODS" Amidst the health giving air of the Pine Woods

15

Telephone · 66 Woodhall Spa.

The Kinema In The Woods c.1931

always held between third and fourth fingers like the notorious theatre critic Kenneth Tynan. Unlike Tynan however, this was born of necessity rather than affectation. When only four years old, Sylvia badly burned her hands in a fire. Attended to by some Victorian quack, her hands were tightly bandaged for so long that by the time the dressings came off, the newly formed flesh of her thumbs had fused with the palms. There her thumbs remained, lifeless, each curled up asleep in the belly of her hand never to move again. As a young boy I would watch her eight fingers in action. It was fascinating to see her open a tin of cat food, peel an apple or light a match. Sometimes I would secretly try to imitate her – clumsily opening doors, picking up a pen and trying to eat a biscuit without dropping it. It was an early lesson in empathy.

Sylvia's weakness for cats meant that with every new visit to Woodhall we'd discover a new litter – a dozen or so mangy bags

Jack

of fur darting around the room, scratching at our ankles, vying for love and attention. As the sole occupant of a council house, Sylvia found her passion bound by regulations. The Lincolnshire authorities took a dim view of all the interbreeding; theirs was a one cat per household rule. After the officials had threatened her with eviction yet again, Sylvia would gather every last bundle of fur, stuff them in a bag and send them to a watery grave in the coffee-coloured eddies of the River Humber. It was the only way she knew.

The only one to escape the drownings was Jack, clearly her favourite. Despite the ever changing cat population, he was easy to spot. A broken spring somewhere had furnished Jack with a miscreant tongue. It hung out helplessly, unable to find its way home. From one angle Jack was parched, and from another he was the village idiot. Even at a naive age I sensed the pathos of this wretched creature. A cat should be independent, haughty, aloof; Jack received only pity and I think he felt it. And that's how I remember them, Sylvia and Jack, a freakshow of loneliness and broken body parts.

Sylvia had been dead a good while before Dad and I summoned the courage to clear out her old house. A hoarder of heroic proportions, she had left us a mammoth task. Armed with sandwiches, teabags and chocolate biscuits we got to work in early spring, boxing up the precious things, dumping whatever was beyond salvation and haggling with the knocking boys over sideboards, iron-framed beds and chipped crockery. It seemed a heartless endeavour: the rapid disposal of the evidence of a life, of a quiet existence that we barely understood, a funeral with scant attendance. What *did* she ever do with her life?

On the third day of clearing, Dad drove to Lincoln for the reading of the will, leaving me in the kitchen on my hands and knees, scraping thirty-year-old cat shit from under the cabinets and cooker. He returned a few hours later and dropped a brown paper package into my hands.

'For you,' he said, and went off to make tea.

I pulled off stiff brown wrapping paper to reveal a glass-fronted box, ten inches long and four inches wide. Inside lay a familiar object, once a prize exhibit in Sylvia's house. Somewhere in time it had disappeared, swallowed up no doubt by her mountains of ephemera. Encased within, nestled amongst faded purple material lay a flamboyant moustache, similar in style to that worn by the great Catalonian surrealist Salvador Dali. The hair had been pinned and waxed to hold it in place. Accompanying it was an old metal disc attached to a thin chain. On it, in spidery handwriting were etched the words:

Trust Absolute Unconditional

'So, what is it?' asked my dad, clattering around in the kitchen. He wandered in with two steaming mugs and let out an involuntary snort. 'Oh. That! I remember that daft thing on her mantelpiece. Don't worry, she left you some money as well.'

'But why leave this for *me*?' I asked, expecting an explanation: Dad had an answer for everything. He swallowed a mouthful of tea and thought for a while.

'It's obvious, isn't it? She knew how much you enjoyed collecting things when you were little. All those tea and cigarette cards you obsessed over. It must be part of a collector's set. Somewhere out there are dozens of other moustaches: the walrus, pencil, handlebar…an estranged family, waiting for the tragic death of a great aunt to reunite them, like characters in an Agatha Christie.'

'Do you really think–'

'No son, I'm kidding.'

After this he seemed to show little interest in the matter and disappeared upstairs. The adolescent in me had shrugged his shoulders too but secretly I was thrilled.

Later that evening, against mild protestations from my dad, I re-opened sealed boxes destined for charity shops, pulling out kitchen cutlery, Sylvia's collection of Whimsy figurines and dog-eared books bearing such titles as *Angel Guardians* and *Waves Of Spirit*.

Finally I found what I was looking for, a pile of old magazines. Idly thumbing through them the previous day I'd found slips of paper tucked into her favourite pages, noting a knitting pattern here or a recipe for Spotted Dick there. There was one article in particular that had caught my eye but I'd been sidetracked by other chores and dad had cleared the box away. Here it was, on page 37 of a 1963 copy of *Lincolnshire Life*:

> Between 1884 and 1912, a local freakshow, Oddfellow's Casino, travelled the length and breadth of England. A magic-cum-freakshow, it heralded such characters as Dogboy, the Laughing Lady and the Midget Chefs.
>
> Its leader, Ambrose Oddfellow, and his wife, known simply as 'K', are noted as great hero figures of the time. One celebrated story even reports how Ambrose removed and auctioned off his moustache to save an accordionist from crippling gambling debts.
>
> The Casino's last ever full performance is recorded in the Travellers' Almanac as some time in the Winter of 1901 when, during the climax of the show, 'K' was tragically killed at the hands of a clumsy knife-thrower. Unable to recover from the loss Oddfellow abandoned the group, seeking solace at first in the whisky bottle then later in his beloved alchemy.
>
> The old cinema in Woodhall Spa, which was once home to this unusual troupe of performers, served briefly as a concert pavilion in the 1910s but went through its final transformation in 1957 when it changed its name to the Kinema in the Woods. Legend has it that the letter 'K' was used out of respect for the late Oddfellow's wife. It is still there today showing old movies in the pines, seven days a week. I think Oddfellow would have approved.
>
> R. Brelsford

Hay!

It's a rare old sight and sound in these days of combine harvesting . . . the clatter and clanking of the threshing machine going full pelt like this one at Mr. S. C. Brown's Glebe Farm, West Halton. The six men in the picture, oblivious of the camera, are toiling and sweating as a glint of sunshine spotlights the ever-growing mountain of straw bales.

I read and re-read the story, trying to imagine this larger-than-life character hosting his twisted carnival on stage at the Kinema in the Woods. If the article was to be believed – and I really wanted it to be true – I was now the proud owner of not just any old common or garden variety boxed moustache, but one that belonged to Woodhall Spa's legendary resident. I was resolute in finding out all I could about Ambrose Oddfellow. Over the ensuing years his moustache would become my obsession.

A few weeks after Sylvia's funeral I went to visit friends in Brighton for the first time. It was a shock to the system.

I was born at the end of the Sixties in Scunthorpe, a depressed steel mining town known sarcastically as Sunny Scunny. During his sixth birthday party my best friend James heard the news that his father had been killed in an explosion at a local chemical plant in Flixborough. Twenty-eight people lost their lives. For months after I was haunted by the screams of James' mother.

When I was eight my family moved to Doncaster, a depressed mining town in Yorkshire. During the year-long miners' strike of 1984 I would see families sat outside their homes selling their possessions just to raise enough money to feed themselves. By my teens I yearned to escape these troubled northern towns and see the world. At eighteen I enrolled for polytechnic, packed my bags and moved to a big city: Coventry. I should have done my research. Once a boomtown manufacturing cars, by the Eighties Coventry had hit the skids and become one of the poorest cities in the UK. Its best-known cultural export was ska band The Specials whose

Dr. Godfrey's
Cordial

Lincolnshire Life records that in 1867 over half the opium imported into the UK at that time went to Lincolnshire. An investigation uncovered the cause: Dr. Godfrey's Cordial. Most households in Lincolnshire were in possession of the stuff and using it to heal everything from pleurisy to loose stools. Dr. Godfrey would sell it in bulk to the old ladies in the villages, who scraped a living baby-sitting for labouring families and would administer Dr. Godfrey's cordial to keep their babies quiet. On the parents' return Dr. Godfrey's would be offered to them too as a pick-me up. What was in the good doctor's cordial? A heady mix of treacle, sassafras and opium. Old ladies, it appears, were the pushers of their day.

single *Ghost Town* accurately portrayed Coventry as miserable and violent. I lived there for four long years studying geography. My final year field trip was a week long tour of depressed industrial towns of Yorkshire.

For a northern boy in his early twenties and still wet behind the ears, Brighton was overwhelming. I'd stumbled on an exotic seaside town that welcomed me with open arms. Like Woodhall Spa, Brighton had first come into fashion as a health resort, offering its seawater as cure-all for those foolish enough to drink it or hardy enough to tiptoe barefoot across the stone beach and plunge into its cold waters. It was Dr Richard Russell who, in the 1750s, published *A Dissertation on the Use of Sea-Water in the Affections of the Glands*, claiming that seawater could be taken medicinally and have the same curative effects as spa waters. While some still bathe daily in Brighton's sea for good health, the practise of imbibing this saline brew has fallen out of favour.

After the reign of its portly pleasure seeker, the Prince Regent, Brighton moved into the entertainment business. It was now a tourist town populated by poseurs, dandies, misfits and lost souls. Brighton had become a place where postmen dressed as Rockabillys, estate agents sported muttonchops and piercings, drag queens queued for strawberries in the supermarkets and a celebrity boxer wandered the streets in jodhpurs, spats and monocle. To the further delight of a testosterone-fueled Doncaster lad, Brighton seemed to have sex on the brain. There were adult shops on the high street, S&M dungeons in shop basements, and kinky clubs and brothels seemingly down every side street. On the seafront, in an area known as The Bushes men skulked, some kicking the night off with a "mercy mission" (the ancient tradition of pleasuring an old timer) before getting down to more serious business.

To top it off Brighton was almost comically eccentric. In an area called North Laine, a man passed me by with French loaves strapped to his head like helicopter blades. Near the seafront a group of occultists called Thee Temple ov Psychick Youth, led by a man called Genesis P.Orridge, formed a ring around the Royal Pavilion in an attempt to levitate it. The police shooed them away before they had a chance to cause any "major structural damage." In a local café I overheard a man in his mid-forties casually reply to his friend, when asked what he'd done that day:

'Not much, I went skateboarding this morning and spent the afternoon carving a butt plug out of ginger for my girlfriend.'

But it wasn't all posturing and frivolities. Brighton had once been the Queen of Slaughtering Places – home to mobster razor attacks, the battling Mods and Rockers, the IRA bombing of the Grand Hotel, shady slum landlords, arson attacks and an unidentified head in a bag at the Horse and Groom pub. There was an underlying darkness to the place. Why else would the Great Beast, Aleister Crowley, have ended up being cremated here?

At the end of my visit, intoxicated by the town's decadence and liberal spirit, I was invited to a picnic on a warm Sunday morning in Queen's Park where I was befriended by Hippy Lilly, who approached me for a light. She was a pale-skinned goddess in a flimsy green cotton dress, with long auburn hair, fishnet stockings and Dr. Marten boots. That afternoon we sat and talked beneath the soft trees. In the crepuscular light of a sinking sun we scoured the beach for skimming stones. With each missile that skipped the waves, leaving little rings in its wake, we laid bare a secret. As the moon rose we were holding hands. By morning we were lovers.

I had been seduced, the proverbial fly in the web. I'd rolled into an exotic land with a moustache in my bag and a mystery to solve. But what do such things matter when you've been taken in hand by an enigmatic and beautiful woman?

NOWT EV'R 'APPENS IN DONNY

My old home of Doncaster, affectionately known to its residents as Donny, has long been the butt of the joke. Once a Roman town of some significance, its fate seems to have been sealed by the comedy world. In the Eighties sitcom *Blackadder*, the Earl of Doncaster was talked about with derisive sniggers. In the Nineties Doncaster's Hotel Swanky was the holiday destination of Rik Mayall and Ade Edmondson in *Bottom*. In his live shows and Radio 4 comedy programme, Count Arthur Strong mentions his days teaching at the "Doncaster Academy for Dramatic Arts." Need an ironic name for a university? Doncaster's just the ticket.

It's not alone of course. "Come, friendly bombs, and fall on

Slough," wrote John Betjeman in 1937 in response to the heartless industrialisation of the town; Milton Keynes still gets a ribbing for its New Town banality and the likes of poor old Bognor Regis and Grimsby suffer the indignation of simply sounding like awful places to go (whether they are or not is another matter). So what is it about Donny that merits such teasing? As an old friend once suggested, 'nowt ev'r 'appens in Donny.' And perhaps he was right. Doncaster does have something of an identity crisis. When an international airport was opened in 2005 the best name the authorities could come up with was Robin Hood Airport, inspired by a minor character from the Robin Hood legends called David of Doncaster, whose only noted characteristics were being grumpy and having no ears. They might as well have called it Braveheart or George Harrison.

In fact Doncaster's best anecdote is a story about a man struggling to find a story about Doncaster. This tale has passed from bar to bar, from generation to generation, like a family heirloom. It begins when portly Mancunian comedian, Bernard Manning, turns up in the late Seventies to appear at the Doncaster Catholic Working Men's Club. Arriving at the venue early afternoon to set up, Manning gets talking to the barman:

'So what's been happening in Doncaster then?'

'Nowt,' comes the barman's reply.

'C'mon,' says Manning, 'something must have happened.'

'Naa. You're in Donny mate. Nowt ev'r 'appens in Donny.'

'Listen, I need *something*. I like to start me set with a bit of a local gag, you know to get 'em all warmed up. Give me something.'

There is a pregnant pause.

'Welllllll...someone nicked our telly last week but –'

'That's great. Ta mate.'

That evening Manning takes to the stage. Directly behind him, a large crucifix with Jesus nailed to it hangs on the wall.

'Good evening Doncaster,' Manning begins. Then, turning to point at the crucifix, he says: 'I see you got the bastard who nicked your telly.'

TWO

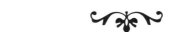

In which I stumble upon a
secret underground club and we
learn about the most dangerous
book in the world.

A CABARET OF MISFITS

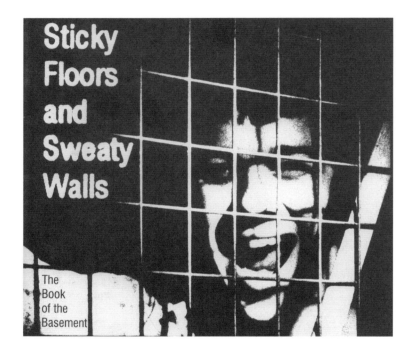

"A tiny hidden entrance disappearing behind stately Regency fanciers. Down the steps. Duck under the doorway at least four inches shorter than myself. Squeeze past the bouncers. Deliver 50p and there I was, in a catacomb of vice that would draw me back again and again for the next seven years, leaving my clothes smelling of pub toilets, eight deep at the bar, a toilet mirror like something at the funfair and Weird Glen..."

Ian 'Curly' Carter (from *Sticky Floors and Sweaty Walls*)

C utting through the centre of Brighton is Grand Parade, a wide Georgian road that takes in the glass-fronted University Arts Building and Victoria Gardens before confusion sets in and it gets swallowed up by the Old Steine. It is along this main artery of the city that many are swept towards the seafront and the Palace Pier. From here some visitors head east or west in search of frappuccinos, flip-flops and greasy chips. Others continue straight ahead to promenade the iron-limbed no-man's-land that straddles beach and sea, where Penny Falls rattle, dodgems collide and starlings pulsate in great clouds at sunset. Visitors to Brighton might deny it but what they've all really come for is the soft rhythm of water on stones, the unbroken horizon and that great mass of rolling blue-grey that soothes the soul, fires the heart and, as Euripides wrote, "washes away man's ills." There is, as they say, something in the water.

North of the Palace Pier at the Old Steine stands Victoria Fountain. Around the base lies a mass of broken boulders, discovered in 1823 by workmen digging in the area. These are sarsen rocks from the Marlborough Downs, a source of hard sandstone used by Neolithic Man to build part of Stonehenge. Thousands of years ago these stones were dragged to Brighton, creating a stone circle that once overlooked the grey waters of the Channel for some mysterious, sacred purpose.

The arrival of Victoria Fountain in 1846 came as a disappointment to the residents of Brighton, many of whom felt it had deprived them of a good hanging. Public executions had once been held at the Old Steine on market days to guarantee good crowds, but with the Capital Punishment Amendment Act just around the corner, the building of the fountain coincided with an end to these bloodthirsty and riotous events. The previous year had drawn record numbers to witness the hanging of Owen Parsons for murdering his boss; Parsons had bludgeoned the man to death with a spade after a bitter disagreement over wages. On the day of the hanging many in the large crowd came armed with rotten fruit which they pitched at the condemned man. As his body swung from the gallows amidst the jeers and fermented missiles, Parsons breathed his last and the crowd emitted a huge cheer. Legend has it that the crack of his broken neck could be heard as far away as Hove.

Once it was over the crowds dispersed, but not everyone lost interest. As Parsons' lifeless body was cut from the noose, his left hand was savagely hacked off by the hangman, Matthew Comstock, and sold to the highest bidder of a small group of shady individuals. The new owner would take it home to be dried, pickled and transformed into a Hand of Glory. Such sinister charms were highly sought after in the 1800s by thieves

Victoria Fountain

The Hand of Glory

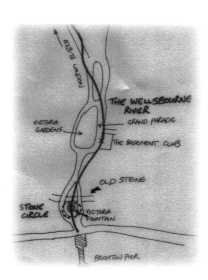

Let those who rest
more deeply sleep,
Let those awake
their vigils keep.
Oh, Hand of Glory,
shed thy light,
Direct us to our
spoils tonight.

Eighteenth-century incantation

and burglars who believed that, when burned as a candle, the hand could unlock any door and render the occupants of a house paralysed. The belief in the power of the Hand of Glory was so fervent that villains were known to murder "innocents" or even pregnant women so as to make candles from the arms of their unborn babies.

Underneath Grand Parade, winding its way from London Road to the seafront is the Wellsbourne, Brighton's lost river that still flows deep below the soil and tarmac. Nowadays it only makes its presence felt in extreme floods but in 1850 the Wellsbourne wreaked havoc. After a vicious storm one afternoon in May this raging torrent of water swept up siblings Emily and Hector Gregs who were playing by its edge, and deposited their lifeless forms by Victoria Fountain. The children's bodies were recovered after the storm had abated but their hands were never found. They had been sold to the highest bidder.

In the 1990s Grand Parade was guardian to a different kind of underground secret: a hidden club, with a stone archway leading to a dank pit of cheap garden furniture, sweat-drenched walls and choking heat. It was a venue called the Basement, where *Debaser* rumbled in the guts of the speakers and skinny figures skulked behind plumes of tobacco smoke.

The great to the god-awful passed through the Basement over the years. When U2 played to a handful of people, diminutive Bono had to be perched on a box so the audience could see him. The Basement attracted its rock & roll wannabes too. One permanent fixture was Weird Glen, decked out in Jim Morrison leathers, John Lennon glasses and a Brian May hairdo. Legend had it that Glen had been the sole manufacturer of LSD for the whole of Sussex until a dodgy batch turned his brain to semolina. After this Glen became increasingly odd, striding around the Basement with a wild, hungry look, his face pulsating with tics. He once spent an entire evening standing at the back of the dance floor licking up the sweat that dribbled down the walls.

I'd been living in Brighton for a few weeks. Renting a room in a hilly area of colourful terraced houses known as Hanover, I had signed on, made a half-hearted attempt to find a proper job and spent my afternoons busking on the seafront to earn a crust. For the time being Oddfellow's moustache lay undisturbed on top of my wardrobe, overshadowed by a new obsession: Hippy Lilly. Thanks to her, the Basement had become my home from home. The pair of us would go most lunchtimes to eat cheap pizzas in the gloom. In the evenings we'd meet Lilly's friends there, dance to indie classics and stumble home stupefied by cheap lager.

The club was host to all kinds of happenings. Sometimes we'd wander in to find a few Goths sitting around eating jelly and wander out again. On other nights there would be cult films, music quizzes, S&M clubs and comedy nights. One warm Tuesday evening Lilly and I poked our heads in to find a packed audience transfixed by a short, suited man wearing a briefcase on his head.

'Welcome to the Zincbar,' said the bouncer on the door as we hung there. 'Fortnightly amateur cabaret. Brighton's answer to *The Gong Show*. A right fucking shambles it is too,' he confided. On the stage the suited man now appeared to be feeding a shaving foam ice-cream to a photo of Joan Crawford. From that moment, I was hooked.

The Zincbar was hosted by Adrian Bunting. A cocky man in his mid twenties sporting a ludicrous hat, Adrian would swagger on stage, cigarette and pint in hand. He dispensed with light banter and gags in favour of shouting until his voice was hoarse, imploring us to adore each act like they were God's chosen ones. When it came to peddling shoddy goods, Adrian was a terrific salesman.

The rules of the Zincbar were simple: anyone – no matter how intoxicated or psychotic – was welcome to get up for six minutes and have a go at entertaining us whichever way they saw fit. And heaven help any poor drunken sod who heckled. Adrian would get up close and shout in their face:

'IF YOU THINK YOU CAN DO ANY BETTER WHY DON'T YOU COME UP HERE NOW AND SHOW US WHAT YOU'RE MADE OF? EITHER THAT OR SHUT THE FUCK UP.' And if the heckling continued, Adrian would resort to violence.

As well as constant fresh servings of unpredictable performers, the Zincbar had its regulars, each a legend within the venue's hallowed walls. The first act on was always Marty, an intense former college professor with a Brooklyn drawl, the sleeves of his old bomber jacket rolled up to facilitate his arms' wild gesticulations. For decades Marty had roamed from Greenwich Village to the squats of Paris and London, publishing underground books, lecturing and performing. He was always looking for the next "centre of great revolution." In his autumn years he settled in Brighton. Just after 9pm, Marty's disheveled figure would weave through the audience towards the stage. He would ramble and rant, preaching his sermon, his narratives ranging from mathematics and world history to the occult sciences, swerving off into random anecdotes until the story's initial thread seemed lost forever. While the rest

Zincbar host, Adrian Bunting

of the acts existed merely for our entertainment, Marty sought to impart some cosmic wisdom our way.

Dave Suit was the Zincbar's resident Situationist. Embodying both Gilbert *and* George, he was short and wiry with a slowly greying quiff and enveloped in an air of mischief and melancholia. He had started as a performer in the working men's clubs of London in the late Eighties with a young medical student called Harry Hill, the two of them clowning around on stage with silly props and routines that made sense only to them. One night, standing at the urinals after a performance in which he'd been playing about with plastic farm animals and a birdcage, Dave was approached by an angry red-faced man:

'I don't know what the fuck it was you were doing on the stage tonight but if I ever see you or that bald bloke again I'm going to kill you both.'

At subsequent performances Dave and Harry opted to slip out the back door once the show was over.

The Zincbar had provided Dave Suit with a more natural home for his act. Spurred on by its host, Dave's situationist performances became even odder. He never spoke on stage, choosing instead to perform with a shirt and tie on his head, a briefcase or, on one occasion, a cardboard fireplace. His act was frequently conceived on the way to the venue, inspired by whatever singular object he found. One of Dave Suit's many unforgettable performances involved a swivel chair (rescued from a tip) and a bottle of whisky. To the accompaniment of a Barry White soundtrack he spun round in the chair, shirt and tie on his head, taking generous swigs from the bottle until he fell into the lap of an attractive girl in the front row and threw up on her. On another occasion he took a novelty soap hand (grope-on-a-rope) and, dangling it like a fob

The legendary Dave Suit with a fireplace on his head

watch, tried to hypnotise the audience and send us into a deep sleep. There followed a bungled attempt to steal our wallets which made Lilly snort with laugher. As the Wellsbourne flowed deep below us that night, both audience and performer were blissfully unaware that Dave Suit had unwittingly evoked the spirit of the Hand of Glory.

Captain Turbot was the only act I've ever seen who managed to get worse with experience. Dressed in chef's trousers and vest, this guy tried everything: comedy, juggling, mime, robotics and rapping, each more hopeless than the last. Finally the Captain resorted to just sitting on stage wanking. And crying. We adored his performances. It was like watching somebody else acting out your own worst nightmares, and empowering to know that whatever happened if you went on stage, it would never be as bad as it was for the Captain. And I did get up on stage. My shaking hands clutching a page of scribbled notes, I stepped into the limelight for the first time. Something compelled me to stand there and tell my stories: my first teenage hangover, a bizarre summer job at Harrods, misadventures in Coventry with stoners and car thieves. At the Zincbar I couldn't be a spectator. I wanted to be part of this cabaret of misfits, these novelty acts for the broken-hearted. I wanted to belong.

WEIRD GLEN

AND

THE MOST DANGEROUS BOOK IN THE WORLD

It was Weird Glen who introduced me to the most dangerous book in the world late one night after the Zincbar, when the offer of free booze lured a gaggle of us back to his flat. Glen's disturbed and chaotic mind cast its shadow into every corner of the room. His bed was weighed down by a heap of mould-encrusted plates and dirty clothes that made me wonder when he'd last slept.

As Lilly and I helped ourselves to the contents of Glen's drinks cabinet, he let loose a diatribe of anarchist philosophies and conspiracy theories, before handing me a pamphlet he had written entitled *Revolution and the Number 23*. Then casually he cast into my lap the most dangerous book in the world.

'Changed my life, man,' he said, facial muscles twitching. 'It's all there, pages 39 to 45.' Suddenly he turned around as if addressing some disembodied voice. 'What? Did you say something?' then turned back to face me. 'Uh. It's all there. Changed my life.'

The object of his life's transformation was *The Anarchist Cookbook*. Its pages contained detailed instructions for the manufacture of illegal drugs, electronic bugging devices, explosives and weaponry. Whether you wanted to make a Molotov Cocktail or heroin, the book provided diagrams, recipes

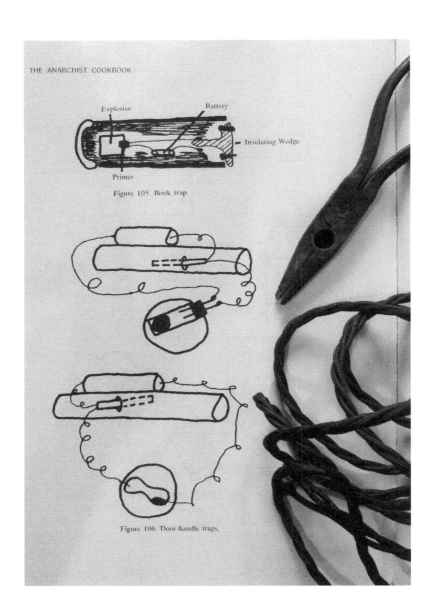

THE ANARCHIST COOKBOOK

Explosive · Battery · Insulating Wedge · Primer

Figure 105. Book trap.

Figure 106. Door-handle traps.

and practical, almost paternal advice from the author – "as a revolutionary, your job is to rally popular support, not to alienate people. For this reason do not steal from small stores."

Described as a manual of terror on its initial publication in 1971, *The Anarchist Cookbook* was, according to its author William Powell, written not for radical fringe groups but for the "silent majority" to educate and empower themselves.

While publication ceased in 2000, it's not difficult to pick up a copy. A few weeks after 9/11 I found one at a car boot sale and, recalling that odd drunken night at Glen's, felt compelled to buy it. As I wandered home flicking through illustrations showing how to convert a shotgun into a grenade launcher or booby trap a bridge, I wondered how many acts of terrorism had been committed because of the object I held in my hand.

But here's the curious thing. Critics and conspiracy theorists have repeatedly claimed that Powell was commissioned to write the book by the US government as a means of taking out some of the "enemies of the state" by their own dirty tactics. Powell was the son of a powerful bureaucrat in the UN and soon after publication claimed to have had a swift conversion to Christianity and denounced his handiwork. Experts claim Powell's book is full of dangerous inconsistencies, with bombs that self-detonate, and drugs that leave permanent brain damage.

Like the arsenic-laced "book that could kill" in *The Name Of The Rose*, was *The Anarchist Cookbook* really designed to harm the unwitting reader?

'Changed my life, man,' Glen had said in reference to the pages which offered detailed instruction for the home manufacture of LSD. Did Weird Glen fry his brains through negligence or was he a victim of the most dangerous book in the world?

THREE

In which I receive
ectoplasmic healing and we
learn about the errant
Fox sisters.

ENTER THE SPIRIT WORLD

Born and bred in Brighton, Hippy Lilly belonged to an embattled species, the genuine local family. One of the few who had stayed the course in recent decades, hers remained unmoved by spiralling house prices, over-priced lattes and a lack of real jobs. After Lilly's father did a vanishing act in the early Seventies, one of the ways that her mother, Margery, scraped a living was to dive for wedding and engagement rings underneath the pier. Not those lost through misfortune down the cracks of the wooden floorboards but rings flung by the jilted, the cuckolded and abused. Smart as a whip, Margery had calculated the rough trajectory of a ring cast in anger from the far end of the structure. Every fortnight she would don her wetsuit, swim to the end of the Palace Pier, dive into the grey brine and retrieve her small bounty, selling it back to the shady jewellers in the narrow streets of The Lanes. This helped pay to keep Lilly clothed and fed, and earned Margery a nickname: the Brighton Mermaid.

Lilly was as Ida Arnold describes herself in Greene's famous novel, "like those sticks of rock, bite it all the way down, you'll still read Brighton." Inheriting her mother's survival skills, she hosted themed parties, ran the door at a seafront nightclub and did life-modelling at the university, earning enough to keep her in tobacco, lentils and nail polish. And while a quiet dependence on pot sometimes made her agoraphobic or distracted, she seemed to know everyone of interest in Brighton and was universally adored. Lilly was my first full-blown love affair. She introduced me to secret late-night drinking holes populated by fishermen and professional drunks and taught me how to cheat on the pier's Dolphin Derby game. She also brought me a new gift almost daily: a cult Sixties paperback, an old piece of vinyl, a mobile she had made from flotsam and jetsam off the beach. To her I was a novelty, the new kid in town who had charmed her with his dry northern manner and naivety. To me, Lilly was a goddess who led me through the backstreets and twittens of Brighton from one adventure to another.

Brighton wasn't known as the graveyard of ambition for nothing. Its residents loitered in the cafés and bars, full of good intentions. They'd talk endlessly about writing a novel or making a film, but somehow never seemed to find the time to even get started. I was another who'd succumbed to the myriad distractions that Brighton had to offer, now immersed in its nightlife, counterculture and a new relationship. It was Lilly who kept reminding me of the promise I'd made to find out more about Ambrose Oddfellow and my strange bequeathment. She was fascinated by the moustache too, for different reasons. It served as a symbolic connection to a father she barely remembered, a man who had, according to her mother, once sported "a walrus in a state of some distress."

One afternoon I came home to find that Lilly had taken Oddfellow's moustache down from the top of my wardrobe, placed it upright on the mantelpiece, and surrounded it with a collection of Hag Stones - doughnut-like pebbles she'd taken from the beach - to "protect it from evil spirits". Like my great aunt, Lilly was a firm believer in the spirit world, and often spent her Sunday mornings at a spiritualist church. Ever the space cadet she loved the place and relayed to me conversations she'd had there with her late grandmother and a favourite uncle who'd once cut the Queen Mum's hair. For Lilly it made perfect sense for me to join her at a spiritual service, as a means of making direct contact with my great aunt or Ambrose Oddfellow. She felt sure I'd "get a result." In the throes of my first real love affair, and still with no clear idea of where to start my investigations into Oddfellow's moustache, how could I say no? Besides, I reasoned, it'd give me another story to tell at the Zincbar.

The Brighton National Spiritualist Church was situated halfway up Edward Street, an area of the town best known for its law courts, police station and American Express building. With its grey-brown stone windowless exterior, the Brutalist design of the church made it almost inconspicuous, save for the soft curves and strange orange logo which hung above its entrance.

Services at the church ran twice a week. Lilly took me along on the Sunday, with the promise of a pub roast dinner afterwards. At first it all seemed surprisingly similar to a Christian church service except praise was given not to God, but to "The Greater Vibration." We sat in rows of hard chairs singing, 'all things bright and beautiful, The Greater Vibration made them all' until a female clairvoyant in deep blue crushed velvet took to the stage and began to channel the spirits. One by one, members of the congregation were reunited with departed relatives, lost loved ones and even dead pets. Through the clairvoyant the spirits revealed their insightful knowledge of one man's painful knee operation and his wife's love of biscuits. Another couple were chastised for not cleaning out their shed. The spirits' love of domestic trivia knew no bounds. This continued for a good hour but neither Lilly nor I were singled out. It had all seemed quite harmless. I thought that'd be the end of it but over our Sunday roast Lilly said:

'Oh, no, it doesn't work like that. You've got to keep coming until the spirits know you're sincere.'

While my belief in The Greater Vibration never passed first

base, persistence finally paid off. It was during our fourth or fifth visit that my moment came. A guest clairvoyant was down from Yorkshire – Clarence Hausman, a burly gentleman in an ill-fitting double-breasted suit and with a penchant for theatrical shaky hands. Clarence had clocked me at the back in my leather jacket and corduroy cap and was now staring in my direction.

'Young man at the back. Stand up please.'

I stood.

'Speak your name loud and clear for The Greater Vibration.'

'My name is David Bramwell.'

Clarence's hands began to shake.

'The vibrations are strong this morning David. I'm picking up, I'm picking up…Russia?'

Clarence clearly had me down as a Commie.

'Er, no.'

'Good!' he said enthusiastically, 'I'm getting Russia, Russia… Russian politics?'

'Er, no.'

'Yes! Good! I'm getting Russia…Russian politics…shipping?'

'Er…no.'

'Yes! Good. That's right! Of course you've been to Russia?'

'No.'

There was a pause as Clarence nodded sagely.

'You have relatives in Norwich?'

Where did that come from?

'No.'

Clarence changed tack: 'With whom do you wish to make contact?'

'My Great Aunt Sylvia and a man called Ambrose Oddfellow.'

'Your father…grandfather?'

'No.'

He didn't appear to be listening. By now his hands were a blur.

'Your grandfather is coming through. He has a message for you. A sensitive issue from your childhood. He feels it's important this reaches you. Are you ready for the message from your grandfather David?'

'Yes.'

'The message is, when you were young, you worried about your ears. Is this correct?'

'Yes.'

It was such a relief to lie.

'He says not to worry son. Just let it all go. Does this help?'

'Yes, thank you,' I said and sat down, wondering for the first time in my life if I had jug ears. For the next ten minutes I couldn't catch Lilly's eye; she seemed to be searching for something at the bottom of her handbag.

Undeterred by our experiences at the church, Lilly's next suggestion was the Saltdean Séance, a few miles out of town. Though she herself hadn't been before, she had it on good authority from her spiritual friends that it was the real deal. This time she felt *certain* I'd "get a result."

Our unlikely clairvoyant for the evening was a builder called Bernard, all gold jewellery and fat fingers. The other seekers of truth were the regulars, eight mousy middle-aged women. Bernard prepared us for the experience with a few simple rules:

NO CROSSING OF LEGS
NO BREAKING THE CIRCLE
NO JEWELLERY
NO FLASH PHOTOGRAPHY

Lilly and I dutifully removed our watches and rings and sat opposite each other in a tight circle of chairs. Black plastic sheeting had been taped across the windows to bar any hint of daylight. In the centre of the circle was a small table. Underneath lay an assortment of bells, balls and rattles.

'For the spirit children to play with,' said one of the women. On top of the table sat a cone with fluorescent strips across the top and bottom.

'For channelling psychic energy,' another woman explained.

The lights were turned out and a taped medley of Victorian music hall numbers began to play.

I sang along to *Daisy Daisy* and *Roll Out The Barrel* as best I could with Bernard barking at us all to sing louder "to raise the spirits' energy." Within a few minutes he was making grunting sounds. This was taken as a good sign. The tape was turned off. There was silence and darkness and then a disembodied voice rang out.

'Good evening. I am Sir, your spirit guide for the night. Do not be alarmed by what you see and hear tonight.'

'Do you hear the voice coming through the ceiling?' the woman next to me whispered.

'We have two new members,' bellowed Sir. 'Welcome. What are your names?'

Lilly and I responded accordingly.

'Good. You are most welcome. David, why are you here?'

'I'm trying to make contact with my Great Aunt Sylvia and a man called Ambrose Oddfellow...do you know them?' I asked.

'Ha! The spirit world is a place of almost infinite nameless souls David. If your relatives wish to converse with you, they will seek you out. But it may take time. I suggest you come back regularly. That is all I can say. Now, do you have any questions Lilly?'

'Erm...does time exist in the spirit world?' Lilly asked sweetly.

'Good question. The spirits like you Lilly, you have an inquiring mind. I suggest you also come back regularly. But to answer your question, no, here we only remember the moment. Everything just is. We just are. We are here to teach and for you to learn. We no longer use or understand the concept of time. In fact this is something I was discussing with the group only last week.' I did wonder how Sir could remember last week if he couldn't understand time, but chose to keep quiet. Bernard was not the kind of man to get on the wrong side of. And besides, I was having fun.

The next spirit to manifest was James, a Victorian drag queen performer. He sounded uncannily similar to Sir but was more aggressive and addressed each of the regulars simply as "woman."

'WOMAN!' he bellowed at one of the females in the circle, 'the spirits are displeased. You have not made a good effort in sealing the room. We cannot manifest unless the room is in total darkness. Go and deal with it WOMAN!'

A tiny chink of light had appeared in the gloom where the black plastic sheeting had peeled away. One of the party got up, fumbled through the dark over to the window and remained there for the rest of the night with her hand pressed against it. Without warning something brushed past my shoulder. A bell rang, and a soft ball dropped in my lap.

'The spirit children are playing amongst you,' bellowed James, 'do not move.' The fluorescent cone began to float in the air and the table started to shake. A scrape of wood on floorboards sounded, as if something heavy had been picked up. But whichever spirit was doing this had either been at the bottle or forgotten to wear his glasses because all of a sudden:

'Shit! My knee!' cried out the lady next to me, as something thudded into her.

'SILENCE WOMAN!' yelled James, 'if the spirits offer you pain, accept with good grace. There is a reason for all things.'

'Oooofff!' Someone on the other side of the circle had been winded.

The third spirit to manifest was Gladys. She too sounded just like Sir and was here to offer us psychic healing. We were led up one at a time to Bernard, and as I stood there in the blackness

something slimy spattered onto my face.

'What was that?' I whispered to the woman next to me after I had sat down, concerned that it was Bernard's saliva.

'Ectoplasm,' she replied, 'it's a healing force.'

After three hours it was over and the lights went on. Bernard had to be roused from a deep slumber.

'Wh…what happened?' he asked.

'It's been a good one,' the lady next to him said. As my eyes adjusted to the light I looked around the circle. The sobbing woman next to me had a bleeding knee. And it became clear what had happened to the winded lady – she'd had a chair placed upside down on her lap. As we were leaving Lilly whispered:

'When I went up for the ectoplasmic healing, Bernard tried to touch my tits.'

Over the following months my confidence on stage at the Zincbar grew as I regaled the crowd with tales of séances, flying chairs, encounters with my dead grandfather and Bernard's wandering hands. When Adrian began calling me the "Zinc Bard" I knew I'd been welcomed into the freakshow's Hall of Fame. And while now certain that dabbling with the spirit world would not "get a result", it had rekindled the desire to continue my quest in earnest. So one morning, with my rucksack packed and moustache carefully wedged at the bottom in bubble wrap, I collected a hire car, picked up Lilly on Brighton seafront and headed out of town. We were on our way to Woodhall Spa.

ORIGINS OF THE VICTORIAN SÉANCE

In his chintzy living room in Saltdean, Bernard was performing a parlour trick that can be traced directly to the antics of two young girls, Kate and Maggie Fox. In Hydesville, New York in the 1840s, the teenagers began to complain of a spirit "rapping" in their bedroom. The girls soon worked out a way to communicate with the spirit using one tap for yes, two for no and employing numbers for letters of the alphabet. The spirit's name, they discovered, was Mr Splitfoot, an old moniker for the devil, who later transformed into Charles Rosma, a peddler who claimed to have been murdered in the house five years before the Fox family settled in.

Such was the growing belief in the girls' psychic powers that previous occupants of the house were tracked down and investigated by various neighbours. The general consensus was that the murder had been committed by a former tenant called Bell. While his guilt couldn't be proven, Bell was nevertheless ostracised by the community.

Within a few years Maggie and Kate, managed by their older sister Leah, set themselves up as mediums and soon achieved an immense fortune. Clairvoyancy quickly caught on. By the 1850s thousands of Americans were claiming to have psychic powers, though it was mainly women playing the role of mediums. For those with enough steel, it was an opportunity for fame and status in a patriarchal society. For others it was a chance to speak their minds and promote such popular causes as equal rights for women and the Temperance Movement.

Many stepped forward to challenge the growing number of celebrity mediums and clairvoyants. Harry Houdini made it his primary mission later in life to expose "phony mediums." Despite his success and the existence of a mail order catalogue that blatantly peddled fake hands and bottles of ectoplasm, vast numbers of staunch believers could not be swayed.

In 1888, one night at the New York Academy of Music, Kate and Maggie (now with drink problems and having fallen out with their sister Leah) decided to spill the beans. Both were feeling deep remorse for their years of deception. Before a large audience Maggie revealed their simple means of creating a seemingly disembodied rapping sound: the sisters had learned how to crack their toe joints. They died friendless and penniless a few years later, though it wasn't until the 1920s that the popularity of séances finally began to wane.

The tricksters and illusionists are still among us. To keep us entertained. To keep us guessing. In the Seventies Uri Geller amassed a million-dollar empire and cult following by claiming that extra terrestrials gave him paranormal powers to bend spoons. Less likely to convince the public with his spoon-bending on stage, Geller took his cutlery out of the clubs and into chat shows, where audiences were disarmed by his apparent sincerity. From here it was a only a small step for a new breed of TV magicians to dress up their tricks as scientific demonstrations of mind control. And do we still fall for it? Of course we do. The show must go on.

FOUR

In which I travel to the
familiar flatlands of
Lincolnshire and we learn
of exotic caravan sites and
secret societies.

YELLOW-BELLIED WONDERLAND

L incolnshire can be a bleak, empty place. By the time we'd passed Peterborough, the landscape had transformed into flatlands, clusters of redbrick hamlets and eerily silent villages. But what Lincolnshire lacks by way of rolling hills and great cities it makes up for with such sensational place names as Snitterby, Wymeswold, Scrivelsby, Whisby and Bag Enderby. Other village names seem perfectly paired together on roadsigns – Fulletby Belchford, Ashby Puerorum, Minting Gauntby – Edwardian characters from a lost Saki story. Some, like Antons Gowt, sound like a story in themselves.

At the risk of offending my lover, the spirit world had been abandoned in favour of a road trip. Lilly had expressed disappointment at my "reading" at the spiritualist church and tried to persuade me to give it another try.

'The guest clairvoyants are of mixed quality,' she'd explained unconvincingly.

Truth be told, I was beginning to find the cosmic beliefs of some of Brighton's residents a little trying, Lilly's included. Instead, I'd taken a trip to Brighton library. Trawling through books on freakshows and Victoriana revealed that Oddfellow's Casino had been a side attraction to the Price and Powell Circus during the late 1880s. It then appeared with the Lord George Sanger Circus and had performed in Brighton in 1892. I also found mentions of an Ambrose Strange and Oddfellow's Oddities, which may well have been the same freakshow. Name changing was a common practice to keep audiences coming back.

A flurry of letter-writing paid off too, eliciting a reply from Roy

The Kinema in the Woods

Slater*, archivist and author of several books on Woodhall Spa. Roy was willing to shed light on my investigations into Ambrose. He was also keen to see the moustache. No further excuse was needed. I'd been feeling nostalgic for Lincolnshire's familiar landscape.

Lilly and I booked into the Jubilee Caravan Park, a haunt of my childhood holidays. She had never been in a caravan before and examined every nook and cranny, unfolding seats into beds and opening all available drawers. I had the impression she'd barely left Brighton while growing up but I didn't like to ask; Lilly hated being pitied for experiences she'd supposedly missed out on. After unpacking we took a swim in the open-air pool then walked the mile or so down the tree-lined Stixwould Road to the village. Lilly bought me an oil painting of a hot-air balloon in a junk shop and I found a book of old postcards of Woodhall for her. At teatime, arm in arm, we wandered back to the caravan to

*Roy asked to remain anonymous. This is not his real name.

The Italianate style of Jubilee Caravan Park

get ready for our big night out, a showing of *Sunset Boulevard* at the Kinema in the Woods.

Half a mile into the forest, beyond the abandoned spa baths in hospital turquoise, lurked the magnificent movie house: a mock Tudor scout hut bathed in red fairy lights. Entering the Kinema again after all those years, I felt a burst of childish delight and squeezed Lilly's hand. A Union Jack hung high in the main auditorium above the gold lamé curtains. Art Deco lights in the ceiling shone down like bloodshot eyes.

'It's magnificent,' whispered Lilly. As the lights dimmed and the adverts began, I tried to imagine the freakshow that had once performed there, with Ambrose Oddfellow on the stage regaling the crowd with incredible feats of memory and performers The Midget Chefs cooking up their alchemical brew. Soon though, the film drew us in.

JUBILEE
CARAVAN PARK

In years to come, in some corner of a sodden field that is forever England, my ghost will sit on a paisley-cushioned foam settee wolfing down a plate of Chunky Chicken and tinned peas while rain beats against my tin home like a drum roll. I wouldn't have it any other way. My love for England, its tangled briars, small brown birds, purple carpeted heathlands and damp forest floors, was forged through family caravan holidays. Over the years we tugged our metal crate from the windswept corridors of the North Yorkshire Moors to scorched corners of the New Forest. And, apart from one horrifying night during my sexually charged teens when my mother bellowed, 'David will you PLEASE STOP ROCKING THE CARAVAN!' I loved every minute of it.

While these trips opened up a passion for the homeland it has to be said that caravan sites are rarely things of beauty. Rows of static boxes squatting constipated in a grey field are still a depressingly common sight in England. But then there's Jubilee Park.

In the late nineteenth century Woodhall's divorced baroness, Lady Weigall, had built the vast Petwood Estate on the village outskirts and, inspired by visits to Japan and Italy, sculpted acres of garden with lakes, temples, stone statues, lawns and an open-air pool. After Weigall's death, the estate became a hotel and a main road divided the gardens leaving an oasis of pillars, pergolas and walkways on the far side. All this became part of the caravan site. With the exception of a Seventies prefab monstrosity carelessly placed by the pool, Jubilee remains a miniature Portmeirion for happy campers.

For an hour Lilly and I held hands in the dark, lost in the movie right up to the moment where Swanson slits her wrists and Holden is on his way back to the old mansion to surrender to her poisoned soul. Abruptly the film stopped and an intermission sign blazed across the screen. Then it rose up: the Mighty Compton organ. Controlling the instrument was a Ronnie Corbett lookalike with parted hair, gigantic glasses and a Pringle jumper. He fondled and caressed the keys like an overzealous masseur. As the organ kicked into life, the audience were treated to a ten-minute medley of music hall standards before the lights fell once more and we returned to the melodrama.

The next morning, in a cottage on the outskirts of the village, we met Roy Slater, an ageing queen with Art Garfunkel hair. He offered us "exotic herbal teas" while his dog busied itself round our ankles, looking up occasionally to bark at every passing car.

'So you're the lad with the moustache? Can I see it?' Roy said. I opened my bag and handed him the box.

'My god, it's a beast!' he boomed. My arrival with the moustache was, according to Roy, 'like turning up at the Pope's house with the Holy Grail in an Asda carrier bag.'

'Well, well!' he kept repeating, 'I never thought I'd clap eyes on the damn thing.'

I let Roy take a few photos of my precious heirloom then showed him the article about Oddfellow's Casino I'd kept from Lincolnshire Life. Roy glanced over it, nodding and shaking his head in equal measure.

Lincolnshire Life, February 1963   **37**

which saw the death of the
l scientist Galileo, but on
same year was born a boy
come the greatest scientist
ige.
ried when he was 37, but
as dead, leaving behind his
a posthumous child. Young
so tiny and feeble that two
AKENHAM'S house at North
ne, as he was not expected
ed any of this tonic medicine
of or without its help Isaac
be old age of 85.
rious son, who rose to fame
arly life makes a fascinating
itirely non-scientific, or have
ie fuse-wire-bulb changing

ive and also very shrewd
clor Rector of North Witham
through an intermediary (he
onsented on condition that
given a parcel of land from

M

c gained some property, but
ie ward of his grandmother,
pe Manor.
and after learning the three
on and Stoke, he was sent to
s a boarder, though he had
Clark, apothecary, next door

ective boy, but still possessed
ticked by a bigger boy, Isaac
ew of the rest of his school-
ippesed to have started his
his opponent was still ahead
ot down to his studies, and
iool.
bination, a dreamer and also
He was always making things
s mechnical toys must have
mates. He watched workmen
vay to Gonerby, then went
ide a replica in miniature,
ented a gadget which utilized
the wind had stopped.

STRANGE BUT TRUE

Those Odd Fellows Behind The Kinema

Between 1884 and 1912, a local freakshow, known as the Oddfellow's Casino, travelled the length and breadth of England. A magic-cum-freak show, it heralded such characters as Dogboy, the Laughing Lady and the Midget Chefs.

Its leader Ambrose Oddfellow and his wife (known simply as K) are noted as great hero figures of the times; one celebrated story reports how Oddfellow even removed and auctioned off his famous trademark moustache in order to save an accordionist from crippling gambling debts.

The Casino's last ever full performance is recorded in 'the Travellers Almanac' as some time in the winter of 1901 when, during the climax of the show, 'K' was tragically killed at the hands of a drunken knife-thrower. Unable to recover from the loss, Oddfellow abandoned the group, seeking solace at first in the whisky bottle, and then later, in his beloved alchemy.

The old cinema in Woodhall Spa, which was once home to this unusual troupe of performers, served briefly as a Concert Pavilion in the 1910s but went through its final transformation in 1957, when it changed its name for the last time to the 'Kinema in the Woods', the K, legend has it, in respect to the late Oddfellow's wife. It is still there today, showing old movies amongst the pines, seven days a week. I think Oddfellow would have approved.

R Brelsford.

His tutor there soon discovered that his new student was

Oddfellow's Casino, Roy confirmed, had settled in Woodhall Spa in 1889. Having charmed Lady Weigall, Oddfellow and his troupe had been allowed to reside in the grounds of her stately pile, Petwood House. For many years Ambrose was the man about town, eventually taking over as Master of the Order of Oddfellows. This was a Masonic-style group with a branch in Woodhall and whose name, many years previously, Ambrose had adopted as his moniker. All had been going well until the death of his wife in a knife-throwing accident.

'He had a bit of a breakdown,' Roy explained, 'hit the bottle, something he was prone to do, and disappeared for some time. Ambrose returned claiming to have had some mystical experience out in the Wolds. After this he was a changed man. He never drank again, took a vow of chastity, became a vegan – pretty radical for the time – and resigned from the group. Not his own freakshow, as your magazine suggests, but the Order of Oddfellows. It was after this that he set up his own gnostic cult.'

I was struggling to keep up, and unsure, from Roy's inscrutable expression, whether he was just making it all up for his own amusement.

'How do you know all this stuff about him?' I asked.

'Oh, the Order of Oddfellows is not the secretive society people think we are.'

'You're one of them?'

'I head the local branch here in Woodhall.'

'Like the Masons?' Lilly asked.

'We share some of the Freemasons' ritual practices but we're very different. We're an open group. Anyone can join,' Roy said.

'And these stories about Ambrose…'

'Are all there in the books at the Lodge. And before you ask, no, they are not for public scrutiny,' Roy said pompously.

'So how do I join?'

'Are you a resident of Woodhall Spa?'

'No, but…'

'Rules are rules, son.'

'So why did Ambrose leave the Order of Oddfellows?' asked Lilly, sensing my irritation at Roy's patronising tone.

'Back then the Order of Oddfellows was tied in with the church. Ambrose evidently lost faith in the doctrine of the church but had some kind of religious epiphany. It's all there in the motto of his cult.'

'Which is?' I asked.

'I thought you'd have figured that out by now. It's been under your nose all this time,' he said, pointing at the moustache.

TRUST ABSOLUTE UNCONDITIONAL

Before I could respond, Roy threw me a knowing look.

'It means trust in your experiences dear boy, absolutely and unconditionally. His cult was based around the central principle of gnosticism, experience over belief. When Carl Jung was asked if he believed in God he replied, "I don't believe in God, I know God." That's a classic gnostic response. If you doubt your experiences, well, why not doubt your doubt? And if you're going to doubt your doubt…well you'll be up your own arsehole before you can say Jack Robinson. That's gnosticism in a nutshell, no need for the middle man between you and the divine.'

'So was Ambrose some kind of spiritual guru?' Lilly asked.

'Who knows what kind of man he was? Chances are he was exploiting those less fortunate than him. In those days there was no political correctness. Give birth to a three-legged dwarf and you'd stick him in Oddfellow's Casino. Ambrose may have been another charlatan exploiting those around him, making a good deal of money by passing himself off as a spiritual healer. You say your aunt had her hands disfigured by a Victorian quack? Have you considered that it could have been Oddfellow who was responsible? If you couldn't afford a doctor in those days you'd go to people like him for healing. That sort of malpractice happened all the time.'

He paused, to take another sip of his "exotic tea."

'And you've no idea how your relative came to own the moustache?' Roy asked.

'No,' I replied.

'Did you know David's Great Aunt Sylvia?' wondered Lilly.

'No-one really knew Sylvia in Woodhall,' said Roy, 'she kept herself to herself. I seem to recall she was part of some spiritualist group back in the day but they're all long dead. Your great aunt smoked liked a chimney and outlived the lot of them. All you'll get out of Woodhall's residents nowadays is golfing anecdotes.'

The timeless interior of the Kinema

On our way home Lilly and I parked outside Sylvia's old house. A burned out vehicle hunched on the verge by her front window. We sat awhile, silently staring out the window.

As a teenager I'd been remote from Sylvia. Embarrassed by this relic from a bygone era, I'd often refuse family visits to her dirty, cluttered house, preferring to skulk around at home, tinkering at the keys of the old family piano. I felt ashamed of my selfishness. It had been different when I was a boy though. With its musty smells, candles and tarot cards forever scattered around, Sylvia's house had then seemed an enchanted and spooky place. There was once a time when I'd have taken little convincing that she really was a sorceress with the power to contact the dead. A memory came back to me of an afternoon at the Kinema with Sylvia when I was seven, hands stuffed with sticky treats, awaiting the latest adventures of 007. Her stern expression had given way to a smile as she gripped my scrawny arm with her eight fingers.

'This is where I first fell in love,' she said, milky-eyed.

'Do you think Roy was right?' asked Lilly, interrupting my thoughts, 'could Oddfellow have been responsible for your aunt's thumbs? In a village this size they must have known each other.'

I didn't answer. I'd been wondering the same myself.

Across the road, seagulls followed the freshly turned furrows of a farmer's plough like the wake of a ship. It was time to leave.

Despite the gales and lashing rain of a late February evening, the Zincbar was as busy as ever. Adrian stood by the door collecting our pound entry fee, with the same question for everyone that passed through that hallowed basement archway:

'Will you be performing tonight?'

I nodded, a story of my recent adventures in Woodhall safely folded up in my pocket. Adrian reciprocated with a grin.

'Good man Bramwell.'

Weird Glen, in paisley shirt and leather trousers, was circling the venue, hands snaking, as if controlling some invisible glove puppet; Dave Suit stood by the toilets, wrestling with a mountain of plastic bags. Lilly and I settled into our chairs near the front of the stage and, at nine on the dot, Adrian strode up to greet the audience.

'Ladies and gentlemen, welcome to the Zincbar!' he boomed. 'As tradition decrees, for our first act of the night please welcome Marty!'

The mumbling American in his bomber jacket appeared in the gloom to the far right of the stage, winding his way slowly through the tightly packed chairs and tables.

'I've been pondering on a question of late,' he said, 'a question we should all be asking ourselves. What is the difference between dreams and reality? If you accept your dreams as a passionate deep part of you, then they become your myth, you are consciously creating a bible of your own history. That's sacred. And more important than school-learned history. Recounting the story of people, kings, this and that, is stuff you can never know or really need to know. School history takes you away from your personal mythology, your unique power centre. It weakens you, filling you with a slave mentality, dominated by strangers' thoughts and dreams. Many of you are young, you probably don't know what you're after yet but you do know that you want to be honest to your developing philosophy of life. What a miraculous place to be. But what I *really* wanted to talk about tonight was trousers…'

Dave Suit in lab coat and Thatcher mask

Later that evening I regaled the crowd with my latest tale, Captain Turbot delivered an angry rant about his flatmate, and Dave Suit attempted to wrap himself up with plastic bags and gaffa tape to the tune of *I'm Too Sexy for My Shirt*. One act, a short topless man in a Mickey Mouse mask who appeared to be just blowing raspberries, met with hostility from the audience. After two minutes, Adrian bounded on stage:

'For fuck's sake, give him his six minutes. NO HECKLING, you know the rules.' Adrian looked menacingly at a table of drunk students who'd been jeering. It did the trick. Mickey Mouse finished his raspberry-blowing undisturbed.

By the end of the evening my bloodstream was heavily diluted with alcohol, when Adrian came bounding over.

'Listen Bramwell, I'm doing a show in Edinburgh this summer and I need someone to host the Zincbar. It's just for one night and I figured you'd be the best man for the job.'

Marty and Lilly, sitting next to me, nodded their approval.

'Wow! You inherited the moustache of a freakshow host and now you're being asked to host a freakshow!' Lilly giggled, 'that's cosmic!'

While this was an appealing idea, dealing with the Zincbar's rowdy audience for a whole night was not.

'Adrian, I'm flattered you thought of me, but the Zincbar crowd, they can be quite a handful. I'm not sure I could. Look, sorry but no.'

There was a pause as Adrian drew on a cigarette and exhaled a great plume of of smoke.

'Pity,' he said, 'there's £80 in it.'

I broke into a grin.

'Good man.'

THOSE ODD FELLOWS

While Freemasonry is still the best-known of the secret societies, at the end of the nineteenth century the Order of Oddfellows was both more popular and catered to a far greater range of workers. Lacking much of the Freemasons' ceremony and obscure symbolism, all the Order of Oddfellows required was adherence to the motto of Friendship, Love and Truth and belief in a supreme being, though the lack of specificity about this means the being could have been anyone from Jehovah to Bob Marley.

The group was formed in the Middle Ages and probably derives its name from the odd assortment of jobs its members did. It was initially set up to help members find work but later expanded its services to health care and, by the twentieth century, charity work. It could be argued that secret societies such as the Order of Oddfellows invented health insurance.

With the advent of the welfare state much of the purpose of secret societies was lost, and they continue to dwindle in number. It's heartening to know that the Woodhall Spa branch, once run by Ambrose Oddfellow in the late nineteenth century, still meets once a month on Broad Street.

FIVE

In which the world's smallest
theatres come to blows and
we learn the tragic story of
the Hilton sisters.

THE WORLD'S SMALLEST THEATRE

I was beginning to develop a friendship with Marty from the Zincbar. It wasn't always easy; he could be a stubborn old bugger at times. When a local magazine offered to write an article celebrating his life, Marty insisted on being photographed from behind and refused to be interviewed. Instead he demanded that they publish an impenetrable fourteen-page poem he'd written, called *I Am An Embattled Species*. Like so many of the Zincbar's singular performers, however, Marty was a natural enthusiast. He took great delight in popping round to tell me about his latest madcap project. If he wasn't researching another rambling monologue on the mystery of slippers, he was making short films, writing stories or sitting in McDonald's scribbling copious notes about the customers as part of a thesis on "the true nature of humanity."

While Oddfellow's moustache had once stood on my aunt's mantelpiece, now it took pride of place on mine. It had sparked Marty's fascination from his first visit and we'd spent many hours discussing it. When I told him about mine and Lilly's trip to Woodhall and our encounter with Roy Slater, he nodded thoughtfully.

'So Oddfellow was a gnostic was he? Hmmm, good for him,' Marty mused, 'to reach divination through one's own knowledge and experience, not through the money-grabbing sadists in the

Catholic Church. Hardly a popular notion during the first half of the millennium, that's why most of them got wiped out by the Inquisition. Trust, absolute and unconditional? Yes, I think that pretty well sums up the gnostic principle of seeking truth through one's experiences. The Buddhists have a similar approach come to think of it. Strange though, I can't ever recall coming across those words in any religious text.'

I was beginning to believe that everyone in Brighton had a doctorate in Mystical Gubbins.*

'But you still don't know why it was left to you?' Marty said. I shook my head.

He picked up the box and began examining it for the umpteenth time.

'You've heard of Laporte right, the guy Dali was into?' Marty asked.

I shook my head again.

'C'mon David, it's time you gave yourself a proper education. He was the alchemist who invented Natural Magic. He believed that moustaches and eyebrows are like antennae, capable of capturing and transmitting ideas. I always liked that idea. Dali was into it too. He argued that the greatness of the early communists was inversely proportional to the size of their facial hair. Marx and Engels had the most, Lenin had a goatee, Stalin a walrus and Malenkov had none.'

Picking up a pencil and piece of Blu-Tack from my desk, Marty attached the pencil to the side of the moustache's box like a walkie-talkie aerial and, putting it to his ear, began to giggle.

'It's for you, David. A Mr Oddfellow. Says he wants his facial hair back.'

*from Doncaster University

smallest shows on Earth

RESPONDENT
MICHAEL POW

back of Notre Dame.
ear is 6ft long by 6ft
nd about a yard wide.
ludes "the world's
t bar" — redefining
t of the theatre crush-
s well as a chandelier
ck wallpaper.
lunting turns up with
and awaits an audi-
meone turning up is
to start. As he can
ly one spectator, ev-
w is a sell-out.
"audience" balances
on their shoulders.
ating and his co-star,
mith, peer through
t it and perform a
tinute production
icide, which is set in
en.
first performance of
linburgh Festival's
theatrical produc-
cancelled last night
of technical trou-
idiences arriving at
''s Theatre to see the
m performer Robert
in *Elsinore,* a one-
rsion of *Hamlet*

Adrian Bunting – the Zincbar's host – was another of life's great schemers. Inspired by a cheese-fuelled dream he woke up one morning, dismantled his bedside cabinet, painted it blue and turned it into a theatre. On a tight budget of £7.50, speakers, lights and velvet curtains were added, with just enough room inside for three heads, comprising a cast of two and an audience of one. Together, Adrian and actress Clea Smith worked out a short comedic two-hander about suicide. Premiering that year at the Edinburgh Festival Fringe, he introduced The World's Smallest Theatre.

For the first few days Adrian and Clea eked out a living on the streets of Edinburgh. The novelty and popularity of their show led to an invitation to perform in the Pleasance Courtyard, one of the Fringe's main hubs. More importantly, it was always teeming with crowds. Everything was going well for the pair until the arrival of Marcel Steiner. For years Marcel had toured the world with his novelty motorbike and sidecar. Inspired by fellow performer and friend, Ken Campbell, Marcel had converted the sidecar into a sentry box-cum-theatre from which he performed plays. These were no mere excerpts but a full repertoire of theatre shows that included *War and Peace*, *A Tale of Two Cities*, *The Guns of Navarone* and *The Third Man*. The only problem was the name of Marcel's act: The Smallest Theatre in the World.

Within a few hours of Marcel's arrival in Edinburgh, the slanging matches between the two theatre companies began. Adrian stood on one side of the courtyard drumming up support

for his by shouting:

'Ladies and gentlemen, you are currently standing in the world's largest foyer, come experience The World's Smallest Theatre!'

Marcel stood on the other side yelling:

'World's Smallest Theatre? World's Smallest Theatre? How dare you steal my livelihood! Twenty-five years I've been touring the world. You scoundrel!'

'Smallest Theatre in the World?' Adrian would retaliate, 'it's about ten times bigger than mine ladies and gentlemen! Perhaps, Marcel, you should call it SLIGHTLY LARGER THAN THE WORLD'S SMALLEST THEATRE.' Performers, comedians, politicians, the press and even a Norwegian film crew all turned up to witness the tirade of abuse between the pair. August, traditionally a dead month for news stories, had found its prize. But it was all a beautiful scam, dreamed up by Marcel's agent. Behind closed doors the two parties were getting on famously. With Adrian and Marcel charging the press £30 each for an interview, they were both doing rather nicely out of it too.

Press interest gradually faded, until one night Marcel's agent invited Adrian for a stroll to the car park behind the Pleasance Courtyard. In the far corner he lifted up a sheet of tarpaulin and said,

'I think you should see this.' Underneath lay a pile of singed timber, ash, twisted metal parts and a motorbike wheel. It might easily have been mistaken for the burned wreckage of a small motorised theatre. The press were informed and seized upon the story. After that, Adrian's phone didn't stop ringing.

'Did you do it?' the journalists demanded to know.

'I should have done. The bastard deserves it,' Adrian said, 'but no, it wasn't me.' The press now had the quote they needed and the story got the green light. It made the front pages of *The Daily*

THE DAILY TELEGRAPH

NEWS

Picture: JAMES FRASER

THE SMALLEST THEATRE IN THE WORLD

Charred frame of The Smallest Theatre in the Wo

Curtain falls on sideca theatre after small bia:

By Nigel Reynolds

A BATTLE between rival acts at the Edinburgh Festival, both claiming to be the smallest theatre in the world, has been resolved after one of them was destroyed by fire.

Marcel Steiner, who has performed at the festival for 25 years in a motorcycle sidecar to audiences of one, found his "theatre" reduced to ashes on Wednesday night.

His rival, Adrian Bunting, has acted inside a wooden box at three festivals. Both gave performances in the courtyard of the same venue.

Earlier this week Mr Steiner, who calls his play-

house The Smallest Th in the World, threat legal action against his petitor, whose box is n The World's Sma Theatre.

Mr Bunting said at time he would fight action and claimed: could fit 20 of mine in hi

He added yesterday: " very sorry for the gu seems pleasant enough. understand how upse must be."

Mr Steiner said yeste "I've no idea who burne theatre. I can rebuild it I will take about a week."

Marcel Steiner performs Macbeth to an audience of one in his sidecar before it was destroyed by fire

THE GUINNESS BOOK OF RECORDS

33 London Road, Enfield, Middlesex, EN2 6DJ.
Telephone: 0181-367 4567. Fax: 0181-366 7849.

We are writing to you following your telephone call last week.

Having looked through our files it is clear that over the years all of our correspondence on small theatres concerns traditional fixed, stationary theatre buildings. This is still the perception that the average person would have. Most people would consider 'I am going to the theatre' to mean that they were going to be sitting down in a seat in a building.

We have an article from 'The Guardian' dating from August 1992 about a Marcel Steiner, and I imagine that it was possibly he who you were referring to when you mentioned the person who has claimed the title of the world's smallest theatre. Although we do not have any correspondence from him on the matter, I am sure that if we had our reply would have been along similar lines to ours to you. It would seem likely that there are a number of slightly off-beat records of sorts appearing at the Edinburgh Festival without necessarily being items which we would consider for inclusion in The Guinness Book of Records.

We hope that this will be of help to you. Thank you again for your interest.

Yours sincerely,

Nicholas Heath-Brown

Nicholas Heath-Brown
Editor

Telegraph and *The Guardian* that week and the second page of *The Times*. Adrian became a full-blown celebrity in Edinburgh. Meanwhile, Marcel had hot-tailed it to Germany the day after the fire. He had a tour booked, and miraculously appeared to have acquired a new mobile theatre in less than twenty-four hours.

Flushed with success Adrian packed his bags and decided to take The World's Smallest Theatre to the streets of New York. He called me the day before leaving to let me know that I was now the surrogate host of the Zincbar until he returned. If ever.

The thought of stepping into Adrian's shoes was now worrying me even more. I still wasn't sure I had the nerve or charisma to pull it off. Discussing it again with Lilly, she said in her persuasive way:

'David, we've been over this before. You've inherited the moustache of a deceased freakshow host. Adrian offered you the chance to be the host of a modern day freakshow. It's clearly a sign from the universe.'

'Lilly,' I interrupted, 'you know I find that kind of talk irritating.'

'Think about what those three words really mean,' Lilly said, ignoring my cynicism. She paused.

'And think of the money.'

I can't deny it, my first night as the Zincbar's compère was a tad shaky. I got drunk, stuck a fedora on my head, got up on stage, yelled out the name of the next act and got off again. But I wasn't shouted down, booed off or talked over. I didn't even have to hit anybody. Over the next few weeks my confidence grew. I no longer bolted off the stage, I lingered. I dreamed up ludicrous alter egos. Lilly made me a pair of musical pants which played *Buffalo Soldier* when struck. I became Dr Bramwell and his Amazing Reggae Underpants and would wander through the crowd encouraging them to slap my backside. Another night on stage Lilly shaved my head, one quarter every hour, from the beginning to the end of the night. The following fortnight I was up there in drag, with a lit candelabra precariously attached to my head. Fuelled by sufficient quantities of booze I felt untouchable; the perfect ringmaster for a benign circus of misfits. While never admitting it to Lilly, I was even coming round to the idea that

WEDNESDAY 2ND & 16TH FEB

ZINCBAR PERFORMANCE PLATFORM

AT THE BASEMENT BAR. ADMISSION FREE

THURSDAY 10TH FEB

COMEDY AT THE UNION BAR
HARRY HILL & AL MURRAY

time, price & shuttle as Jan 13th

"Harry Hill is Britains finest and funniest new comedian"
THE GUARDIAN

MONDAY 14TH FEB

it was indeed my destiny to follow in the footsteps of Ambrose Oddfellow.

It was the night I did a striptease that things began to go wrong. Having shaken off any last remnants of modesty, to the obligatory soundtrack of *The Stripper* I planned to slowly reveal a limerick written on various body parts. For the finale I would stand naked before the crowd to reveal the punchline written across my genitals. It was, I thought, what they expected of their new host.

The evening began with Marty shuffling through the crowd delivering a haunting monologue on the Battle of the Somme, followed by our resident situationist Dave Suit. Dave lugged a large bucket of plaster of Paris on stage with him. After striking an alarming pose at the back of the stage, he had his girlfriend paint his body with the white goo. Twenty minutes later he'd set solid and remained there for the rest of the night.

Next up was Captain Turbot who did an "expressive movement" somewhere between a lap dance and the onset of appendicitis. At the end he announced his plan to move to South Africa, which was met with a murmur of approval and his biggest ever round of applause. But as the time for my striptease approached, I began to feel strange. The ceiling appeared to be moving, and I became mesmerised by the sudden intensity of the lights. My grip on reality loosening rapidly, the truth sunk in. I was coming up on LSD. There'd been a series of spikings in recent months, clearly the handiwork of Weird Glen. Leaving a pint unattended in the Zincbar had become a risky business. Glen had picked me as his victim that evening.

Once the saucy horn intro of *The Stripper* kicked in it was too late to do anything. On I went. My garments were dispatched one by one, revealing each line on limbs, torso and, finally, my genitals:

There once was a mouse called Keith
Who circumcised boys with his teeth
It wasn't for leisure
Or sexual pleasure
But to get to the cheese underneath.

The applause grew as I stood naked before an appreciative audience. The freakshow and the drugs had me in their grip. ·

It was only then that I noticed a figure sitting in the front row, applauding wildly. How had I not seen him before? He was dressed in a black cape and string vest and brandished a jewelled cane. On his bald pate was a blue tattooed triangle. He was hairless, save for an ornate and perfectly sculpted Daliesque moustache. As he stood up to cheer a soft angelic voice in my head said:

'It's the spirit of Ambrose Oddfellow, here to applaud you for accepting your commission, to follow in his footsteps! Trust your experience David, absolutely and unconditionally.'

Then another voice took over, one of cold reason and logic:

'Calm down. You're just tripping. There's nobody there.' Before I could figure out what or who these voices were, Weird Glen came running towards the stage, naked. Taking my nudity as a cue for an evening of all-in naturism, he rugby-tackled me to the ground. For a moment it seemed like we were in some twisted gay porn film. The lunatics had taken over the asylum. Our naked bodies writhed on the floor and the audience cheered, thinking this was part of the show. As I wrestled in vain to get Glen off me I rolled in something wet. It had an all-too-familiar odour. With growing horror I realised what it was. Dave Suit, trapped in his plaster of Paris prison at the back of the stage for three hours, had pissed himself. When I looked back for the vision of Ambrose Oddfellow, he was gone.

THE HILTON SISTERS

In the early days of the Zincbar, Brighton's cruisy gay bars were amongst the few free-entry places where we could keep drinking late into the night. Once the Zincbar's shambolic cabaret had run its course we'd gatecrash another to keep the booze flowing.

A favourite haunt was the Queen's Arms on George Street, which maintained a constant barrage of round-the-clock cabaret. In one corner, enveloped in a fug of dry ice, were the notorious drag queens Large Marge and Betty Swollocks, miming their way through Broadway tunes and lashing out with acerbic tongues if our attention waned. In another corner, sat below a framed photograph of an Eighties DJ called Bubbles, a gang of lesbians would be having a heated political debate.

It seems fitting that the Queen's Arms was home for Violet and Daisy Hilton, the world's most famous Siamese twins. Born in 1908 to a young unmarried barmaid called Kate Skinner, the twins were pygopagus; joined at the pelvis. Seeing the babies as a potentially lucrative business, the pub's landlady, Mary Hilton, effectively bought them from her employee. Within a few weeks she had picture postcards of the girls printed and selling for tuppence each. Together with her husband Henry, Mary ruled the girls with a rod of iron. She taught them to sing and dance and, when they were old enough, sent them on tours of Europe and Australia

with vaudeville and freakshows. Even up to their late teens the girls were dressed as dolls, with Daisy on violin and Violet at the piano. Quite how badly the twins were mistreated is hard to gauge, though their own accounts portray their adoptive parents as brutish and loveless.

By the late 1920s the Hiltons had moved to America with the riches earned from Daisy and Violet. When Mary died she bequeathed the twins to her daughter Edith as if they were heirlooms, but with the help of a lawyer friend the pair untangled themselves from the abusive Hilton family. With their money and newfound freedom they set up their own tour as the Hilton Sisters Revue, befriending Houdini and Bob Hope on the road.

In 1932 they appeared in Tod Browning's film *Freaks*. Its tagline ran, "Never again will such a story be filmed, as modern science and teratology is rapidly eliminating such blunders of nature from the world."

Freaks had caused untold controversy on its release. Thirty minutes of the film were cut before it was deemed fit to be shown in New York. Even then it was still considered too unpalatable for American audiences and withdrawn shortly afterwards, remaining banned for decades.

While strong accents and wooden acting let it down in places, Browning's film remains a fascinating document of old freakshows and deals sympathetically with its cast of outsiders. It contains one of the most shocking endings ever, mixing horror and Pythonesque humour when the freaks wreak revenge on the evil beauty Cleopatra who has exploited and humiliated them.

'We'll make you one of us,' they chant. The last we see is an amputated Cleopatra with a feathered chest, clucking like a chicken.

While many of the cast only had cameo or showcase roles, Daisy and Violet's subplot explored the tricky subject of how conjoined twins could, individually, find lasting love. This problem was to haunt them throughout their real lives. Violet, the more gregarious of the two, had a number of celebrity boyfriends and made several attempts to marry that were turned down in more than twenty-five US states. Some government offices viewed these marriage applications as cheap publicity stunts, while others refused on moral grounds. Both twins eventually got a taste of marital bliss but for each it was fleeting. For the men at least, it seems likely that these marriages really were more about publicity than true love.

The year after *Freaks* was released, Violet and Daisy returned to England for a tour, harbouring a desire to be reunited with their natural mother who they hadn't seen for over twenty years. They arrived in Brighton to discover that Kate Skinner had died giving birth to her fourth child only a few years after the twins had been born. Heartbroken, they contemplated abandoning the tour but the crowds that greeted them in Brighton convinced the pair to stay and they performed a

sell out show at the Hippodrome.

In 1950 Daisy and Violet appeared in their second film, *Chained for Life*, in which one of them jealously kills the other's lover, leaving the jury with the awkward question of what to do with the innocent party. Like *Freaks*, the film proved too much for a conservative audience and flopped. Having paid for the entire production, Daisy and Violet lost most of their wealth.

Quitting showbiz they set up a hot-dog franchise in Miami. This failed too. By 1962 they were bankrupt and involved in another fruitless venture, a revival tour of *Freaks* that was doing the rounds of cinemas in the US. At a drive-in movie theatre in Charlotte, North Carolina they were callously abandoned by their manager and left penniless with no means of getting home. They remained in Charlotte working in a grocery store and died broke a few years later in the small trailer they'd made their home. True love and lasting happiness had eluded them to the end.

SIX

In which I narrowly escape
death and we learn about
Hag Stones and the curious
Mr P. Orridge.

THE SOMNAMBULIST

Something had changed between Lilly and I. Our little rituals of affection – buying each other a gift each week, posting love letters – had fizzled out. I had become less tolerant of her faddish diets and mystical beliefs; now we seemed to spend our time bickering and falling out over silly things. I was becoming more remote too, distracted by my notoriety at the Zincbar and boozy nights out with new friends. It all came to an abrupt end after Lilly caught me fooling around with another girl at the club one night. Lilly had introduced me to the town and its secrets and now I'd grown tired of her.

'Look at you,' she cried, the night we split up, 'you're getting too big for your own boots.' She paused. 'I still love you. But it's not enough David, it's not enough.'

I still loved her too but tried to carry on as if she'd never existed. I took down the mobile she'd made me and stuffed it in a drawer. The clothes and trinkets she'd left were bagged up for her to collect. I even removed the doughnut-shaped Hag Stones she'd brought me from the beach to "protect" Oddfellow's moustache and threw them in the garden. Back in my room, absent-mindedly, I picked up the moustache and my thoughts turned to Ambrose Oddfellow. Unable to resist drawing parallels between our lives I tried to imagine that we were now connected through the pain of losing the women we loved. But it was a crass comparison and I knew it. Oddfellow had watched his wife die on stage in front of him, the victim of a stunt that had gone wrong. Doubtless as leader of the troupe he would have blamed himself for the tragedy and suffered guilt for the rest of his life. I, however, had just been a prize pillock. And on this realisation the tears came. Lilly was my first true sweetheart and I'd failed to nurture the love between us. I regretted my foolishness. Perhaps, back then, I could have tried to heal things, to regain her trust, but I didn't. It wasn't just my pride that held me back; it was something far more insidious.

Ever since the vision of Oddfellow at the Zincbar, a newfound insomnia had me in its grip. Fatigued and anxious, I was beginning to withdraw from the world, paranoid that the drug spiking had unhinged me. If Weird Glen was still manufacturing LSD with the ingredients from *The Anarchist Cookbook*, would I end up like him I worried, another lonely Brighton casualty, twitching and muttering to myself? Equally worrying, in the twilight hours I'd been revisited by that angelic voice, murmuring: "Trust your experiences David. Absolutely and unconditionally." Exhausted but unable to sleep I took to the streets.

Brighton by night was rarely at peace. Whatever the weather there would be platoons of hen parties, tottering around in deely boppers, nurse outfits and towering heels. Hot on their trail were the prowling hyenas, the booze-fuelled boys battling in the gutters. I kept out of their way, skulking down side streets and alleyways as if shaking off an invisible stalker.

After the clubs had cleared and the drunks and stoners staggered home, the city's atmosphere changed. The streets became the domain of the lost and bewildered, visitors who had stayed out too long and sobered up with the realisation that they were destined to walk the streets or curl up in doorways until the milk train carried them home.

HAG STONES

Brighton's Beach is said to contain 614,600,001 pebbles, though who has counted them all remains a mystery. Amongst the many millions can sometimes be found Hag Stones, the pebble equivalent of a Polo Mint. These are also known as Adder Stones, Goddess Stones, Witches Stones, Serpents' Eggs, Snakes' Eggs and Druids' Glass.

Once believed to have formed from the head of a serpent or sting of an adder, Hag Stones are the Brighton equivalent of a four-leaf clover. Luckier still, Brighton's beaches are amongst the best in the country for finding them, especially if one searches close to the shoreline.

A Hag Stone is thought to have many practical purposes: hang one in your home to prevent a witch from riding your chest or put one in your stable to prevent horse theft. It can also protect against nightmares, whooping cough and snakebite. Local fishermen used Hag Stones as talismans to protect their boats from storms and as charms to help secure large catches of fish. In Victorian times, necklaces of them were sold "for luck" in Brighton and were favoured by women of fishing families. The commonest places to find them in any household were hanging from the bedpost or placed on the mantelpiece, as protection from evil charms.

My nocturnal wanderings led to some strange encounters. Early one morning I stared open-mouthed at an intoxicated couple in the throes of fellatio on a stretch of grass at the Old Steine. They were seemingly oblivious to the small but dedicated crowd who'd gathered to enjoy the show.

Another night, down Queensbury Mews near the West Pier, I was accosted by a Belgian transsexual called Tin Tin who had decorated the exterior of her house with slogans, poetry and a slew of CCTV cameras. She asked me to be her lookout for a little job she needed to perform "to deal with some troublesome neighbours." How could I refuse someone who was prepared to climb onto her roof at four in the morning wearing five-inch heels, carrying a tin of paint? I kept guard for twenty minutes while Tin Tin carefully painted the words "DRUG DEALERS" on her tiles, complete with an arrow pointing to the house behind. Having listened to her complaints of being persecuted by her neighbours, I had a feeling that Tin Tin's artwork wasn't going to help matters. Dropping by a few weeks later to see how she was getting on I found the house boarded up, and the poems, graffiti, cameras and Tin Tin herself all gone. Outside her front door lay a small pile of Hag Stones.

A late night oasis was the Market Diner on Circus Street where the legendary "Gutbuster" satisfied the most ravenous stoners and drunks. Here, Mr Kipling silver foil cases served as ashtrays and the staff had long since learned how to decipher the breakfast orders of incoherent psychopaths. Departing the diner early one morning, fuelled by coffee and tobacco, I found a man lying face down in a pool of blood. He'd lost some teeth, his shirt was ripped and his face was bruised and battered. He cursed under his breath, wheezing and choking as I helped him up and offered to take him home. This fifteen stone or so of semi-dead weight

swore and muttered all the way,

'Gonna kill him…I'll fucking murder him…'

More ranting revealed that he had been in a fist fight with his brother-in-law and come off worse.

His house was at the top of Albion Hill, the cruellest slope in Brighton. After a struggle to find his door key I lugged him inside, cleaned his face and suggested a sobering coffee. He stumbled into the kitchen and began clattering with cups and spoons. The house was sparsely furnished: a few football magazines on the sofa, a

Tin Tin's house

television and a gas fire. It seemed to inform of a bleak existence. I lit a cigarette and looked around for somewhere to flick the ash.

'You got an ashtray?' I asked.

'Use the floor,' he slurred from the kitchen.

'No, I can't do that. I'm sure…'

'I said use the floor. Cunt.'

The universe shifted. Before I knew what was happening he was in front of me wielding a hammer. 'Next time I see you, cunt, I'm going to kill you, stick this fucking hammer in your fucking face.' He was addressing an imaginary foe but swinging the weapon inches from me. I closed my eyes and shook with fear. When I opened them he was gone, back in the kitchen preparing coffee.

'Sugar?' he yelled, almost amicably. Then he was back, slicing the air with the hammer. I felt a draught on my face as he swung it closer and closer, cursing and ranting, projecting his rage on me.

'FUCKING CUNT!' he yelled and gave a mighty swing. I ducked the blow and a warm flow of urine soaked my trousers. He staggered back to the kitchen again as if taking a breather between acts. I knew with absolute certainty that if I stayed a minute longer I'd be dead. I tried to move but couldn't. And then the angelic voice came floating into my head.

'Trust, absolute, unconditional,' it whispered. Power returning to my legs, I fled to the door, desperately trying to remember the shape and style of the door handle before reaching it, terrified I would fumble and fidget before feeling a cold thud splinter my skull. As the mechanism turned smoothly in my hands I said a silent prayer of thanks to the angelic voice and was out of there, tearing back down the hill to my house where I exploded with tears and lay awake in bed until dawn.

I surfaced from my room mid-afternoon, still trembling. I wanted to call Lilly and sob down the phone, inviting her over so she could wrap me up in her arms and tell me it would all be ok. There was a knock at the front door. I ran to open it, my mouth already forming the word,

'Lilly?'

Standing at the door was Marty from the Zincbar, all smiles.

'Hey David, I've had this idea about a film...'

I burst into tears.

As Marty served up coffee and toast I sat shaking in the kitchen.

'Someone tried to murder you. Jesus! Are you hurt?'

I shook my head through the tears.

'What are you doing wandering the streets at night?'

I began to babble:

'I can't sleep Marty. I think I'm losing my mind. People are out to kill me. I keep hearing this voice and–

'David, calm–

'Marty, I saw Ambrose at the Zincbar! He came to see me,' I shouted.

He raised an eyebrow.

'What, the night you and Weird Glen were naked?'

'Yes, but–'

'Weren't you both on LSD that night?'

'Yes but–'

'How are things with Lilly?'

'Don't ask.'

'David, she misses you. Go and see her.'

'I can't Marty. I'm a fuck up.'

Marty put his arm around me.

'Look, I'm going to help, but right now you're in a fragile state. Look after yourself. Get some rest. Please don't do anything stupid,' he said.

So I joined a cult.

GENESIS P.ORRIDGE

AND THEE TEMPLE OV PSYCHICK YOUTH

'The sigil must await its opportunity to act, influencing the patterns of physicality until such time as its encoded intentions can be brought to fruition. It is the seed planted into the uncertainty of future times.'

Paul Cecil

Genesis P. Orridge was once a notorious figure in the UK. A sickly child who had survived several near-death experiences, he later became fascinated by anything that was deemed taboo, shocking or perverse. Establishing himself as a performance artist in 1969 he used bondage for live sex rituals, took paint suppositories and crapped onto canvasses and generally made it his business to get up the noses of Middle England. By the mid Seventies his antics led to Genesis being described by a Tory MP in *The Sun* as a "wrecker of civilisation" which doubtless pleased him.

Genesis's two bands, Throbbing Gristle and Psychic TV, produced a heady mix of hardcore industrial music, field recordings of live rituals and rave beats. Albums seemed to appear monthly and often came with extensive sleeve notes or magazines on topics ranging from the deconstruction of language to the nature of ritual and sex magick. One album sleeve listed "ten reasons to murder." While he enjoyed any opportunity to shock and provoke, Genesis could be reassuringly conservative too. On one occasion a friend dropped by his house to find Genesis and his partner getting ready for bed, wearing matching M&S pyjamas.

Thee Temple ov Psychick Youth (TOPY) was Genesis's cult. It sprang from the burgeoning scene of seekers and subversives

sometimes described as Modern Primitives. Members of the group explored tattooing, piercings, pain and sex rituals, citing these practices as a form of spiritual awakening. One of the key preoccupations of TOPY was the creation of sigils, magical symbols through which spirits or gods may be summoned and utilised. Inspired by the artist Osman Spare, TOPY's members believed sigils could become more potent if their creators added something of themselves. The sigils became works of art through the addition of bodily fluids (particularly semen and blood), skin and even facial hair. Genesis saw himself as the group's leader but power struggles soon led to a rift in the group. On his departure Genesis demanded that the group fold; they didn't. Small outposts of TOPY still exist today and the organisation's influence on the explosion of body modification culture was huge. After all, TOPY's members had been exploring genital piercings, tribal tattoos and scarification at a time when even a nose ring was considered risqué.

On a frosty early morning in February 1991, the police raided Genesis's flat in Brighton's Roundhill Crescent. It seemed inevitable. A Channel 4 *Dispatches* documentary had told of evil cults that were active in Britain. During the programme a woman claimed that a Brighton cult had forced her to undergo an abortion and killed her baby to harness demonic powers. TOPY's symbol flashed up on the screen. The woman said that the ritual took place in the basement of the cult leader's house, "using tiny forceps."

Genesis was out of the country at the time of the raid. He never returned, having been warned that otherwise his children would be taken from him and put into care. But the documentary was misleading, the story perverted by fundamentalist Christians who used inmates from a mental institution in Liverpool as witnesses. Channel 4 issued an apology but it was too late. Genesis had started a new life in America. He did, however, have a watertight defence against the accusations of misconduct in his Brighton basement: the house had no basement.

SEVEN

In which I journey to distant galaxies and we explore secrets of the serpent, DNA and hallucinogenic plants.

THE GNOSTIC CULT

Half a mile east of the Palace Pier stood a once dilapidated children's play area called Peter Pan's Playground, three words which perfectly summed up Brighton. Its residents' adolescence seemed to continue for at least ten years beyond the point when the rest of the country's youth had begun to pursue sensible career choices and parenthood. While other town's nightclubs were the exclusive domain of the young, Brighton's were patronised equally by the young-at-heart. "If it's a good party, why leave early?" was the town's motto. Eventually though, most encountered a career crisis. How to escape the minimum wage vegan café job when you hit middle age and realised your indie band was not destined for greatness? In my town, the only two realistic choices were teaching or alternative health. The latter was usually the softer option.

While Dr Russell's sea water cures had first established Brighton's reputation as a health resort, it was Sake Dean Mahomed who kept it firmly on the map. An Indian entrepreneur with a nose for the latest fad, Sake moved to Brighton in 1814, having already established Britain's first Indian curry house in London. Here he set up a "shampooing" vapour bath that could supposedly cure any ailment. The treatment became so popular that Sake was soon being referred to as Dr Brighton.

Two centuries later, Brighton was packed to the hilt with alternative practitioners offering everything from Reiki and Qigong to herbalism or rolfing. If it was a crisis of the soul you were suffering instead, there were Buddhist orders, pagan circles, meditation groups or even Aleister Crowley's religious sect, Ordo Templi Orientis. And if the town didn't already have a cult or religion to your taste, you could simply start your own.

The breakup with Lilly, my insomnia and the night of the hammer had all been too much. I was in need of a guiding light. My mind, once skeptical of Lilly's "cosmic coincidences", was now susceptible to every portentous sign it could find. After spotting a homemade flyer for a group called the Revolutionary Gnostic Shamanism of the Light in a Brighton café, I felt that I'd hit the jackpot. After all it was a gnostic cult that Ambrose Oddfellow had set up in Woodhall over a century ago. This really did feel like a sign from the universe.

The Revolutionary Gnostic Shamanism of the Light met twice a week in a large Edwardian house opposite Preston Park on the edge of the city centre. The founder of the cult was a long-dead Colombian mystic with a tongue twister of a name. Even now I'm not sure how to pronounce Samael Aun Weor. Keeping the flame alive in Brighton was former postman Adam, a stocky man in his thirties with a pointy ginger beard and eyes ablaze with missionary zeal. Adam's conservative attire belied the tattoos of burning skulls and occult symbols that adorned his body, an indelible reminder of his formative years with Thee Temple ov Psychick Youth. Disillusionment with orgies, drugs and avant garde industrial music led Adam to seek a purer path, using a system that required strict discipline of body and mind. Even the pleasures of the flesh were out of bounds for a Revolutionary Gnostic until one learned to control the orgasmic impulse. Our leader's favourite topic was "not spilling the seed." He could pontificate about the evils of ejaculation for hours.

Adam was a dedicated teacher, full of energy and enthusiasm. Under his tutelage we studied the Kabbalah, dream yoga and Gurdjieff's Fourth Way. After lectures dense with esoteric language and diagrams, we would meditate and rock for hours in our chairs chanting "hamm saa," squeezing the muscle between our genitals and anus to "transform our sexual energy." Over the first few months we remained a motley crew of strong silent women, curious hippies, a few lost souls and myself, believing that I had a destiny to fulfil in being there. But the group seemed to be having

Samael Aun Weor

a positive effect on me. The mental and physical exercises helped me sleep better and the teachings were opening my mind to ideas beyond the realms of scientific rationalism. With my sleep under control, I'd even begun to participate in experiments with lucid dreaming.

'Become a spy of your sleep,' Adam would repeatedly say. 'Be aware of your physical location. Pull your finger or jump in the air with the intention to float. Ask yourself – is this the physical plane or the dream world? If anything unusual happens, you'll know you're in the dream world.'

Every day, as often as I could remember, I would give my middle finger a good yank. This continued for weeks, to no consequence. Then one time I gave my finger a pull and, to my amazement, it stretched like putty. In shock I found myself shivering on top of a skyscraper in a surreal and ever-changing landscape, fresh, alert and frightened by the realisation that I was conscious in a new reality. Despite several further successful episodes of "waking up" in a dream I was never able to remain there for long before sheer astonishment pulled me from it, leaving me awake and breathless.

True, there were elements of the teachings that were challenging. Adam's lecture about a race of giant ants that once ruled the planet was a good one for clearing the room of non-believers, but I took this kind of stuff with a pinch of salt. The principle of gnosticism was, after all, to trust in our experiences, absolutely and unconditionally.

One afternoon Adam turned up at my house, wild-eyed with excitement. He had made contact with another cult of Revolutionary Gnostics in deepest Dorset. Unlikely as it seemed, this group had stumbled on a couple of genuine Colombian shamans living in the local area and was spending its weekends drinking ayahuasca. This powerful South American hallucinogenic

– also known as yage – was said to induce the power of telepathy. Adam had gone to Dorset a sceptic and returned a convert.

'The Dorset group,' he excitedly informed me, 'are on a fast track to enlightenment.' The first of us to be selected for an ayahuasca ceremony were those in our group's inner circle. To be honest, I'm not sure we ever had an outer circle.

An ayahuasca ritual was not something I chose to undertake lightly. After the LSD spiking and insomnia I was cautious about surrendering myself to another powerful psychotropic experience. I began researching yage and its side effects. William Burroughs had travelled deep into Colombia and Peru in the Fifties in search of what he called "the final fix" and wrote up his experiences in *The Yage Letters*. Burroughs' first encounter with the plant seemed deeply unpleasant. He wrote of a "sudden and violent nausea," "a numb dizziness" and concluded:

"Larval beings passed before me in a blue haze, each one giving an obscene mocking squawk. I must have vomited at least six times. I was saying over and over, 'all I want is out of here.'"

I was assuaged by further research, in particular a book called *Essential Substances* which described one of yage's purposes as "finding lost objects, bodies and souls." Now convinced of the existence of realities beyond the material world I reasoned that, if ayahuasca could be used for finding lost souls, I would use it to meet Ambrose Oddfellow in the world of dreams and spirits.

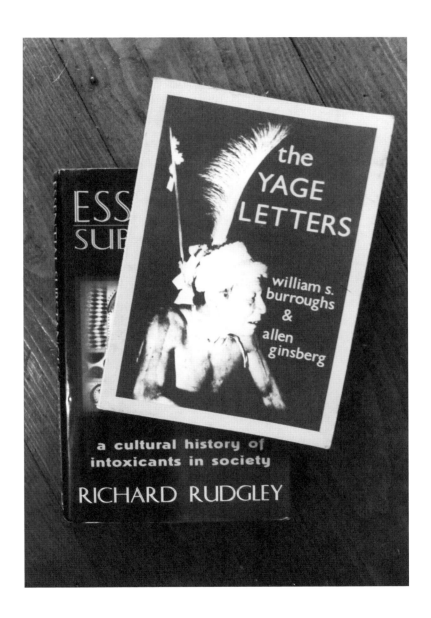

Our first drinking ceremony took place in early spring at a thatched cottage in Piddletrenthide, a stone's throw from the wonderfully named Piddle Inn. The assembled company comprised the two Colombian shamans Radrani and Vasudé, Adam and his wife, five members of the Revolutionary Gnostic Shamanism of the Light and Carl, who ran the Dorset group. The shamans spent the day in the garden boiling the yage vine with another plant that acted as a catalyst, fusing together the male and female plants to give the drug its potency. Inside the cottage we donned white robes, chanted, meditated, fasted, chewed coca leaves and smoked cigarettes as part of the initiation. By evening we were prepared for the journey. A huge bowl of noxious green-brown potion was brought into the room. The shamans drank first, slowly and calmly. I was the last to drink. Vasudé handed over a bowl of ayahuasca and I took my first sip. I felt like I had swallowed the vile dregs of a stagnant old village pond. Retching I grabbed a water bottle, swallowing hard. My stomach turned. Looking back at the bowl I realised there were still another five or six generous mouthfuls to go.

The first experience for most ayahuasca users is the powerful purgative effect. We had lain motionless on the floor in the dark for over an hour before the stampede began, a Mexican wave of people running for the loo, shitting, retching, staggering out and laying down again. I lurched to the bathroom just in time, erupting green liquid. Vomiting helplessly into the basin I saw strips of binary code pouring out of my mouth and an angelic voice drifted into my head whispering,

'You've been spending too long in front of the computer.'

Back in the room the men and women had been separated. The women were in a corner swaying, crying and cradling each other. The men were kneeling on the floor, stoical, eyes closed. I felt dizzy and alone. Panic swept over me. I wanted Lilly to be there to hold me and tell me that she loved me and everything would be all right. Then Vasudé whispered soothing words in my ear in his strong Colombian accent:

'Don't be frightened David. Go with the flow. Remember, the plant is intelligent, more intelligent than you are. Trust it. Let it take you where you need to be. Don't be afraid.'

I turned to thank him for his comforting words but he wasn't there. He was in the far corner of the room, eyes closed. It was my first experience of telepathy.

A little while later Radrani brought us together in the main room of the cottage and said,

'This is the hour when the plant's power is at its strongest. It is the time for learning. Ask your question and you will have an answer.'

I said to the ayahuasca,

'I wish to connect with the spirit of a man called Ambrose Oddfellow?'

Time passed slowly. I regained control over my physical being. Complex fractal patterns swirled before me, worlds within worlds. I journeyed to remote galaxies where I floated in the heavens of a gleaming white planet. I took a walk outside and saw the energy of life shimmer and dance before me as I gazed at the plants and the trees. At other times I felt overwhelmed by a universal power that flipped me around like a corked bottle in a tempest. But the answer to my question never came.

The ceremonies became a regular occurrence. Every fortnight we'd drive to Dorset and follow the same routine: fast, drink, vomit, hallucinate. At the sacred hour I would repeat my request for the plant to help me find Ambrose Oddfellow. But while I was trying to use yage for some pseudo-mystical pursuit, the plant had its own agenda. Ayahuasca could be brutal and scolding like a strict parent. It paraded the skeletons in the closet. I began to see the truth of what I was willing myself to become: a man who wasn't me.

My final drinking ceremony came on a hot day in June. In the early hours of the morning a group of us were meditating in the throes of the drug's effects, when the silence was broken by a woman's scream,

'FIRE!'

We ran outside to see the thatch of the cottage alight. Rich orange flames licked the night sky.

'It's an attack from the Black Lodge!' Adam screamed.

He would later inform me that the Black Lodge was a bunch of cosmic terrorists who loitered around the astral plane looking to cause trouble. I maintain that the fire was caused by the discarded cigarette of a careless hippy.

Within minutes two fire engines and the police had arrived. Adam volunteered to be spokesman for the group. He stepped forward in his white robes and said,

'Nothing to worry about officers, I can explain. We were just communicating with beings from another dimension.'

Tripping heavily I slipped away from the flashing lights, sirens and shouts of the firemen to the darker edges of the garden. As the sounds faded I heard that angelic voice in my head again, urging me to look up and that I would have my answer.

There above the flames of the cottage, up in the night sky, I saw him. He was hanging amongst the stars, bathed in the orange glow and staring down at me. Not Ambrose Oddfellow, but a vision of Christ, floating in space.

THE FINAL
FIX

There is a story that tells how, in 1954, the remote Brazilian Taraucá tribe were shown a couple of movies by a US Air Force captain. He expected them to be thrilled at this modern marvel. But the Tarauaca's response disappointed him.

'The western world has a lot of catching up to do, in comparison with the things we've seen on ayahuasca,' they said. 'Perhaps movies will eventually be replaced by ayahuasca, once it has caught on in the West?'

Ayahuasca is a jungle creeper that twists like a double helix around trees in the Amazon. It has been described as "the spirit vine," "the ladder to the Milky Way" or "the great medicine." It is not, however, a recreational drug. Only a reckless individual would take yage without an ayahuasquero (shaman) to guide them through the intense and sometimes painful journey.

In preparation the bark is mulched and either boiled for a few hours or soaked in cold water. Author Wade Davis described the taste as "the entire jungle ground up and mixed with bile." Taken in isolation the ayahuasca vine will give no effect, but has to be combined with the leaves of another plant containing dimethyltryptamine (DMT). This leads to one of the many mysteries for modern science: with no

knowledge of chemistry how did Amazon people discover, from the millions of different plants in the rainforest, that the combination of these two would create a psychedelic effect?

One person who has tried to answer this is Jeremy Narby. In his book *Cosmic Serpent*, he points out that a primary psychedelic experience is to hallucinate complex patterns. The shamans have long claimed that these patterns play an important role in shaping their society. The decorative art of Brazil's Tukano people is nearly all based around geometric patterns said to represent a reality higher than our own. After years of studying psychotropic plants and having the odd trip himself, Narby came to believe that psychedelic plants take the user's consciousness to a molecular level, a quantum world where biomolecular secrets reveal themselves through patterns. These patterns can manifest as abstract geometric shapes or, more symbolically, as animals. An experienced shaman makes sense of these patterns and uses this information to heal sickness and gain knowledge.

The native people of the Amazon take the idea one step further. They say that the plant itself is the teacher. Asked how they learned to paint or became expert in plant medicine, ayahuasqueros will reply, 'I was taught by ayahuasca.'

After nine years of research Narby returned to the Amazon to find a shaman, Carlos Perez Shuma, who he had met at the beginning of his research. Shuma had previously claimed that the popular symbol of entwining snakes in ayahuasca held secret knowledge. Having at first taken this as fanciful nonsense, Narby came to the conclusion that the serpents were a symbolic representation of DNA. The ayahuasca user is taken to the quantum world, where the DNA itself is the transmitter for information passing between the two worlds of dream/spirit consciousness and human consciousness. Narby explained his findings to the shaman,

'I have discovered that in scientific terms, all the things you told me are true.'

'What took you so long?' the shaman replied.

The ladder to the Milky Way

EIGHT

In which Marty lectures on the true nature of the universe and I pay a visit to England's strangest museum.

MARTY'S LECTURE

The Zincbar had been a Brighton institution for several years before I rolled into town. It started life at a seafront club called The Escape, overlooking the Palace Pier. Unable to persuade the venue to provide any chairs, Adrian bribed a deckchair attendant for a key to his lockup. A master blagger, he then convinced a friend from local newspaper *The Argus* to give him enormous offcuts of paper with which he lined the venue walls. Adrian left out tins of paint and brushes with a sign, "let the people paint." By the end of the night, the Zincbar was decorated with psychedelic art, graffiti and drunken obscenities. Several years on, the venue had been switched, the deckchairs disappeared and the host had been waylaid in America. Otherwise little had changed.

As another typical Zincbar night was about to kick off, Dave Suit appeared at the door, preparing for an act that involved a bag of sugar with a hole in it, a reel of masking tape and a cardboard cutout of Wham! Zincbar regular Robbo sidled up and offered to give me a tattoo on stage as a grand finale. Once I would have leaped at the idea, but lately I'd been feeling less comfortable playing the impulsive extrovert. I decided in favour of an audience sing-along.

As always, Marty was the first to perform that night. He'd prepared a lecture with an overhead projector and slides and came shuffling and muttering through the audience.

'Tonight I want to talk about patterns,' he began. 'If you take a strong hallucinogenic drug you see patterns. People who have religious visions describe patterns. When a quantum physicist increases the magnification of the microscope, eventually all he sees are patterns. When meditating I see patterns. Patterns of increasing complexity. Science has a name for these patterns - fractals. And the mother of them all is the Mandelbrot. For those who don't know, a fractal is any pattern that reveals greater complexity the more you examine it. Like a coastline. Or a tax form. "Infinity in a grain of sand" as Mr Blake understood it. Worlds within worlds.' Marty laid an image on the overhead projector and continued with his monologue.

'Recently I came across a book containing this image of a Bodhisattva. What struck me was the number of patterns contained within it. The more you look the more detail you see. Worlds within worlds. It even looks like a fractal. It led me to examine other religious images.'

Marty began producing more slides.

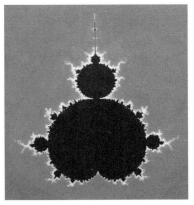

Mandelbrot fractal

Bodhisattva

Hindu God   Madonna with child

'This is a painting of a Hindu god. Look what happens when I slap the fractal on top. Not an exact fit but interesting don't you think? See how closely the head of the Mandelbrot fits with the design of Brahman's headgear. Or the position of his hands with the "hands" of the fractal?

How about this mediaeval Christian painting? Again we're not expecting an exact fit but those two oval shapes by her thighs are rather curiously placed, don't you think?

Or this picture by the surrealist Max Ernst, inspired by hermetic diagrams of the cosmos? Ok, it's clearly about fucking but it does look like a fractal too.

Islam forbade the use of human form when describing god. Do you know what they use instead? Patterns! After many months of research and contemplation I have come to an important realisation – these artists all had the same vision as me but described them using the symbols of their belief system. Math is my belief system, which is why I experience the pattern as a fractal. Those having a genuine mystical experience – scientists, shamans, visionaries, whatever – are seeing the Universe for what it really is: the paradox of infinity expressing itself through the finite. The Universe has far more intelligence than science gives it credit for. It has, I propose, consciously designed itself using fractals.'

'Men Shall Know Nothing of This' Max Ernst

As the night was winding down I found myself sat with Marty.

'How are you keeping David? You seem a lot calmer these days. I was worried about you. The group therapy seems to be helping.' (I'd been economical with the truth about the gnostic cult.)

'Have you seen Lilly?' he continued.

I shook my head. I'd hoped that she would have returned to the Zincbar or I'd see her around town but we hadn't crossed paths since the break-up. Brighton had a way of making you bump into people you didn't want to and missing those that you did.

'Your talk was fascinating,' I said, in earnest. 'Do you really think–'

Marty cut me short.

'Have you found out any more about your heirloom?' he asked.

I shook my head again.

'Thought not. So I got a hunch that you ought to see this.'

He pulled out a small, cheaply made local magazine called *Buzz*. The cover story, "Draks Bak", was about a local man named Drako Zarhazar. He'd had a car crash, lost his memory and was now convalescing. His cover photo – the shaved head and the curled moustache – was immediately and thrillingly familiar.

'Marty, that's who I saw here at the Zincbar that night!'

'Yes, I had a feeling it was,' he grinned.

I felt a sudden, overwhelming sense of relief. It hadn't been a vision of Ambrose Oddfellow who'd sat at the front applauding my nudity, but this man, Drako. I began to read the article. Drako had led an extraordinary life, appearing in films by Andy Warhol and Derek Jarman. He'd even modelled for Dali's famous painting, *The Crucifixion of Christ*.

'You know the painting, right?' Marty chipped in, 'Christ suspended in space on the cross. Dali said it came to him in a cosmic vision.'

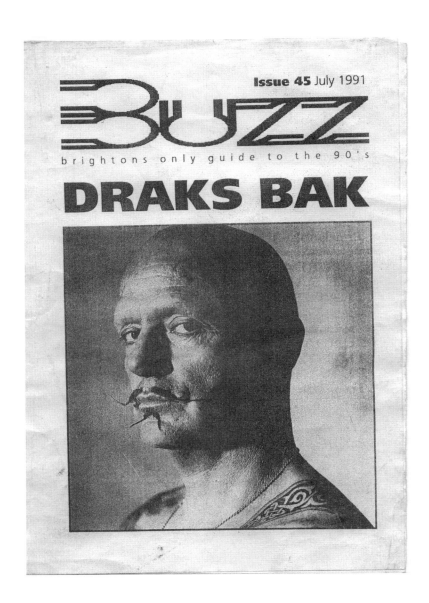

London, and was feted as "One to watch" by Beryl Reid in The Stage. He moved on to ballet with the Moscow State Circus, then the Moulin Rouge in Paris. One day at the poolside, a young lady approached and asked him to go along with her as Salvador Dali had requested an angel! Drako went to the surreal thing's hotel, stripped off, sat for a few drawings, and found himself part of the entourage, eventually modelling for Dali's Crucifixion of Christ.

He removes his hat, exposing a tattooed tri: bald crown - and a healing scar on the side *"Love - to be linked to any changes - is whatever form it shows itself: passion, a: style. To care, to care, to care. To fucking c fucking. It is one of the primal essentials."*

"Is that what's kept you going?" I ask, *"th*

And now the hairs stood up on the back of my neck. The ayahuasca vision of Christ floating in the night sky had left me with a nagging sense of familiarity. It was Dali's Jesus that I'd seen. The cottage fire had even bathed my Jesus in the same orange glow as the painting. But if Dali's muse was the model for the painting, it wasn't Jesus I'd seen hanging in the night sky but Drako. I'd asked the spirit of ayahuasca to locate Oddfellow and it had shown me this man instead, playing the role of Jesus. The coincidences didn't stop there. Drako's accident had happened on the very same day that I'd arrived in Brighton with Oddfellow's moustache. I decided to come clean to Marty about the gnostic cult and Drako's connection with my ayahuasca vision. Marty thought for a while then began to cackle with laughter.

'Well, well, David, perhaps your moustache really is a psychic transmitter. And one with a jealous streak?'

I began to speak but Marty cut me short.

'You roll into Brighton the same day this guy has a car crash and goes into a coma? Classic case of 'this town ain't big enough for the both of us!' Stands to reason, your moustache put a curse on this guy to bump him off! A case of professional jealousy!'

His voice rose to an excited crescendo, 'your insomnia – a result of your complicity in this crime perhaps? MACBETH DOTH MURDER SLEEP!'

'Yeah, very funny Marty,' I said. 'You are joking, right?'

The Pitt Rivers is housed at the back of the University Museum of Natural History on Parks Road in Oxford. With the city's traditional modesty about its treasures, nobody has taken the justifiable opportunity to erect a banner outside proclaiming it to be the UK's most eccentric museum. It's overlooked by most visitors, and unknown to many of the city's residents. And I think that's how the museum would like to keep it. The Pitt Rivers exists for the fanatical anthropologists, the seekers and the occultists.

I once spent a long student summer in my late teens working in Oxford, getting up at 5am to don hairnet and wellies for a glamorous £3 an hour job in an orange juice factory. At the end of the shift I'd sometimes make my way to the museum's quiet corridors, shaking off the putrid perfume of decaying orange pulp to mooch round this treasure trove of bizarre ethnological curiosities.

The gloomy Victorian pile was crammed with hundreds of beautiful old glass cabinets that bore such eye-catching names as "Treatment of Dead Enemies" or "Headhunters Trophies." The artefacts within, individually labelled, were no less thrilling. Some corners of the building were so dark that the curators handed out torches for visitors to explore what lay hidden in the shadows. The torchlight might briefly catch the twisted face of a reclining mummy, a wooden doll filled with nails or a shrivelled foetus in a jar.

Not all the curators at the Pitt Rivers welcomed the thrill seekers who came to ogle at shrunken heads or trepanned skulls. One, however, revelled in it. Eric was a bald skinny man in his fifties with a cheeky sense of humour. He befriended me after my endless hours of loitering and on quiet afternoons gave me tailor-made tours.

'OK, it's headhunters and cannibals today David, so keep your

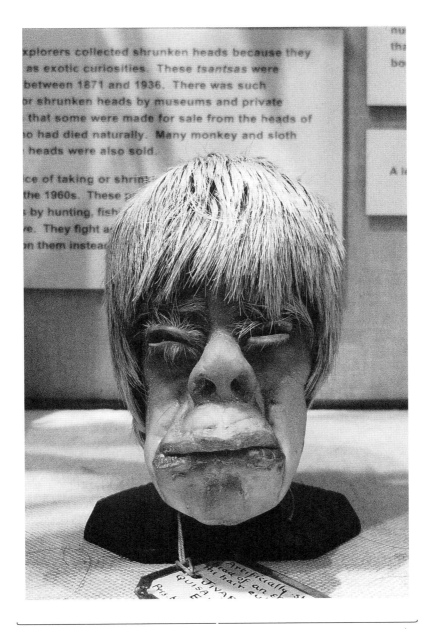

hair on and try not to get into any hot water!' he'd joke. 'I'll start by showing you the chains they used to drag dead bodies out of the ground for rituals.'

On other days I'd be treated to mediaeval torture devices or ancient medical equipment for penis operations, which made my eyes water, and Eric giggle. I have to admit, I did worry about what he got up to in the privacy of his own home.

It had been several years since my last visit to the museum. I was seeing friends in Oxford for the weekend and figured that, if Eric was still there, he'd enjoy examining my own curious relic.

I wasn't disappointed. Eric was thinner, his curved posture more pronounced and he sported a black eye that neither of us mentioned but he was utterly delighted with the moustache.

'Well the box is definitely Victorian,' he said, running his fingers over it, 'and judging by the state of the 'tache, that is too. Trust, Absolute, Unconditional? What's that about?'

'It's the motto for—'

'Sounds like a firm of Jewish solicitors,' he said, giggling. 'So, can we have it?'

'The moustache? Er, no, I—'

'I'm only kidding, son. What do you want to know?'

I told him about the inheritance, the ayahuasca vision and Marty's sniggering insistence that my moustache was an antenna for magic. I was sure he'd poke fun but instead Eric grabbed my arm and led me to a corner of the museum titled "Amulets, Cures and Charms" and "Sympathetic Magic." Inside a cabinet lay a Nigerian juju nut with a label that read "to render the owner invisible." Eric showed me a snake fang from the Congo used for determining a person's guilt in trials, an Oxfordshire charm for warts, a bottle containing a trapped witch from Hove, and many

Silvered & stoppered bottle
said to contain a witch.
Obtained about 1915 from
an old lady living in a
village near HOVE, SUSSEX
she remarked "and they do say
there be a witch in it, and if
you let un out there'll be a
PECK o' trouble."

Pres. by Miss M.A. Murray, 1926

Woman's skull (this),
taken in a raid on a
village by SEMA NAGA
SATAMI, NAGA HILLS.
Pres. by J.H. Hutton

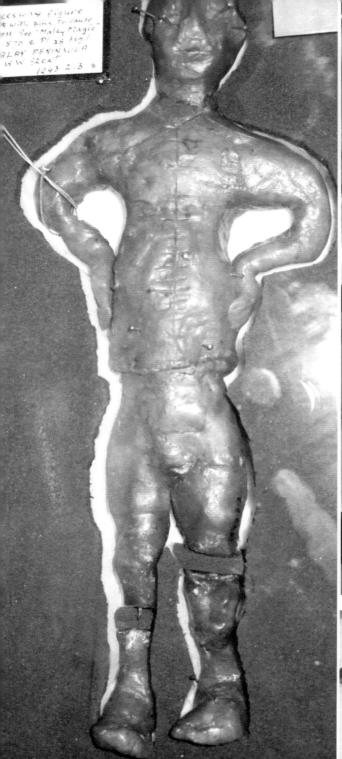

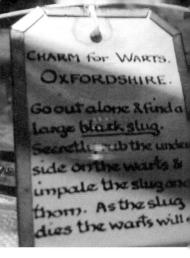

CHARM for WARTS.
OXFORDSHIRE.

Go out alone & find a
large black slug.
Secretly rub the under
side on the warts &
impale the slug on a
thorn. As the slug
dies the warts will...

Amulets, Cures, and Char...

PLEASE D...

Charms against the Evil Eye

EGYPT
1946.8...

other mysterious objects.

'Magic is all about intention. The people who made these gave them a function, a supernatural power. It's practised all over the world. You might ridicule the idea of inanimate objects having special powers but look at the way we fetishise money. It's only bits of metal and paper after all. Scientists might say it's mumbo jumbo but they practise it too. What do you think placebos are? Dr Whatsisface invests the placebo with magic through his words. That's the true meaning of a grimoire: grammar. And if he plays his part convincingly enough, he can heal you. Or rather, you can heal yourself. Same goes with the stuff here. Although in some cases,' he added, 'they have the power to kill.'

Eric opened an unmarked drawer beneath the cabinet to reveal a figure full of pins.

'Beeswax voodoo doll. A fine example of sympathetic magic. The Haitians believe in the power of the witch doctor. Show them one of these with their name on it and they'd be dead in a week. You'll like this David,' he said, opening another drawer. Inside lay what looked like a pair of mating dogs made out of biscuit.

'Copulating gingerbread dogs, one of my recent discoveries.'

'Used for what?'

'Buggered if I know,' Eric replied, closing the drawer.

'Thing is,' he said, pointing at my heirloom, 'this stuff works as long as *someone* believes in it. Right, how do you fancy a tour of our self-mutilation kits, favoured by the Dervishes? We've got this terrific spiked ball for gouging out eyeballs in the service of God!'

Eric grabbed my arm and began to march me towards the stairs to the next floor. Then he paused.

'And if you ask me, it sounds like you do.'

'Do what?' I asked.

'Believe in it.'

NINE

In which I meet a man called
Drako Zarhazar and we
learn how he acquired his
curious name.

THE MAN WITH NO MEMORY

'Hello, have we met before?'

In front of me stood the man who had once applauded my vulgar exhibitionism at the Zincbar. He was in his late sixties, sporting a Fez and make-up, and nonchalantly twirling his moustache. Beneath his cape he wore a black vest, his nipples poking through two little makeshift holes. Pieces of thread were wound tightly around each nipple. An elegant rope was tied around his generously proportioned waist, holding up an enormous pair of faded black trousers. Drako Zarhazar planted three kisses on my cheek and welcomed me in.

The flat was adorned with the same flamboyance and attention to detail as his body. Collages covered the walls and ceilings. Most were pornographic (erect penises and Leonardo Di Caprio featured heavily), mixed with images of Christ, religious aphorisms, Dali prints and a reminder to feed Sado, his black cat. Glass beads hung from doorways. A great layer of dust coated every surface. Sado slept on the sofa next to a small TV which chattered away in French. In the living room, hanging by threads from the ceiling, were hundreds of postcards, photos and letters. It was impossible to see across to the other side of the room for the sheer volume of these mobiles.

'You don't mind me dropping in on you?' I asked, nervously. He spoke slowly.

'Are you a friend of Barnaby's? Have you been here before?'

'No, we've never met before,' I replied, as a mobile of naked

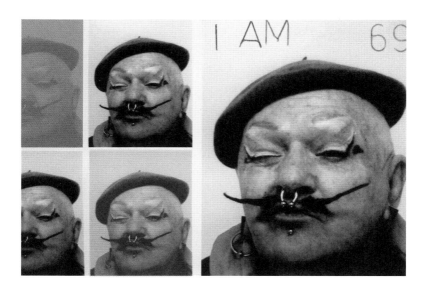

men in cowboy hats gently fluttered around my face.

Drako shuffled into the kitchen, brewed a pot of jasmine tea and beckoned me to sit down in the living room. He didn't show the slightest surprise at my presence.

'Love everything,' he declared, beaming at me.

I sat forward in my chair; I couldn't hold back any longer.

'I came here to ask you something.... does the name Ambrose Oddfellow mean anything to you?'

There was silence. Then Drako replied.

'Nothing, sorry. Should it? The memory machine in my head, it doesn't work any more. Who is he? Have I met him before?'

'But your moustache, what inspired you to grow it?'

'The great Dali!' he said, mimicking Dali's own theatrical voice.

Disappointment hit me hard. The LSD night at the Zincbar, the ayahuasca vision of Drako as Jesus, Marty's magazine, they'd all been leading me here hadn't they? I'd convinced myself that in meeting Drako, I'd have an answer to my inheritance. Now the idea seemed foolish. What was I doing in this strange man's home?

Unable to bear more silence, I tried another question.

'How did you first meet Dali?' Drako's eyes lit up.

'It was 1968! I was dancing in Paris at the Moulin Rouge. Two girls approached me and said, "please come with us. Dali has asked us to bring him an angel. We have chosen you." There he was, the great Salvador Dali in this hotel suite with its own swimming pool, drinking pink champagne. His first word was: "booooooonnnjjjjooouuurrrrrr!!" He asked me to take my clothes off and said, "do you want to come to Port Cadaques with me?" Then he sat down next to me and watched these girls swim naked in the pool. And I'm sitting there politely but couldn't help noticing his arm moving up and down inside his dressing gown. And I thought, here I am in Paris, sat next to the great Salvador Dali, who is having a wank. Isn't life wonderful?'

Once Drako had started, there was no stopping him. His recollections of events before the coma were lucid and colourful. He talked about his year living in Cadaques in Spain, as part of Dali's entourage of "beautiful people," bombed out of his skull on LSD and weed. He described working with Andy Warhol and Derek Jarman and an old flame of his, a cellist who only ever performed naked.

'Everything I have done to my body I have done instinctively,' he declared. 'With the exception of my moustache I shave every hair on my body daily. I am, of course, an instinctive flasher. What I'm wearing now I find aesthetically pleasing.' Without encouragement Drako dropped his trousers. Half the kitchen drawer appeared to be hanging from his genitals. Taking his heavily pierced penis in his hand he giggled – 'I've always wanted

to do this…' Pretending to be at a bar with his cock dangling out of his trousers he said:

'Two pints of beer please,' and burst into a Basil Brush laugh. As we leafed through scrapbooks that showed that Drako had performed and hung out with everyone from Des O' Connor to Keith Richards, it was clear that he had lived a remarkable, if hedonistic, life. His eccentricity was genuine. And the more we talked, the more I sensed a man at peace with the world.

'Love everything,' Drako kept repeating. 'I feel gratitude for every second of life.' He appeared to embody the Buddhist ideal, of living entirely in the moment. I had found a benevolent Kurtz – an eccentric old gentleman who had stumbled upon the secret of happiness.

As I turned to leave I asked Drako if he had any regrets. He shook his head then, after a moment, boomed:

'Actually, yes! When I lived in Cadaques with Dali there was a film made, *The Soft Self-Portrait of Salvador Dali*. There's a marvellous bit where I burst out of an egg. I've never seen it.'

Wanting an excuse to visit him again, I offered to track the film down. Would it be so bad, I asked myself, if all of the madness I'd been through was simply to allow an act of kindness?

That same day, Adrian Bunting finally returned from New York. The World's Smallest Theatre had not been a success. New Yorkers, Adrian discovered, were not interested in putting their heads inside a box on a busy New York street.

'Why don't you just write "mug me please" on your jacket?' one resident suggested sardonically. I thought my ego would take a battering returning the Zincbar to Adrian. On his first week back he got in a punch-up with an act who defecated on the stage. Later that night Dave Suit had *his* drink spiked with LSD. It felt like I was giving back the keys to the asylum.

HOW DRAKO
GOT HIS NAME
(AND OTHER STORIES)

If, during the Nineties, you happened to be at Brighton Station on a Sunday evening you may have had the pleasure of witnessing Neel dressed as a Prozac tablet, Cluedo character or in a floral gimp outfit, heading for the photo booth for his next bizarre creation. For many years Neel created gloriously silly works of art. He spent the week preparing costumes, props and accessories, and then on Sunday evening would head off down the hill for the big event, usually with friends in tow.

I was honoured to be invited to the photo shoot recreating the shower scene from *Psycho*. Neel's friend Gwen, towering 6 foot 5 inches in heels, sat in a bikini behind a makeshift shower curtain. She was spattered with water and blood, screaming and hamming it up while Neel thrust the knife into the booth when the flashes went off. The pair received a warning from the police who thought they were making a porn film.

Neel's most ambitious project was also his last. After ten years he was leaving Brighton and wanted to stage a mock funeral. Having made a coffin he sent invitations to his twenty-four closest friends, asking each of them to come dressed as funeral guests. The invitation read "everyone has to die one day, I'm just organised."

Vicars, undertakers, a grieving widow, the Sally Army and even an Elvis impersonator turned up. After a spot of dutiful mourning and a speech by the deceased, one by one they filed into the photo booth for their picture with Neel's "corpse."

'What fun!' Neel exclaimed, when I saw him a few days before leaving on his travels, 'I'd recommend it to everyone. The

mock funeral is an underrated art form. It should be an annual event like a birthday.'

Neel was one of countless eccentrics I met in Brighton. While most towns can boast of at least one colourful and notorious character, Brighton seemed to cultivate them in Petri dishes. Throughout the Nineties the town had an unofficial mayor: Brian Behan, brother of playwright Brendan, a curmudgeonly old prankster who enjoyed getting his name in the paper. Brian's ritual of taking a daily naked dip in the bracing waters, whatever the weather, meant that he was regularly fished out of the sea by the air-sea rescue team. A devout communist and troublemaker, Brian once famously forced the local council to re-open a seafront toilet after threatening to stage a "mass wee-in" at the town hall.

Another trickster was the

Reverend Rohan Krivaczeck, a talented violinist forced to play weddings to scrape a living. The Reverend was convinced that playing a funeral would be a more profitable and dignified affair. Owing to the lack of any such tradition, he invented *The Guild of Funerary Violinists* and appointed himself Acting President. Krivaczeck then composed dozens of authentic-sounding scores and even wrote a three hundred page book on the subject: *An Incomplete History of the Art of Funerary Violin*. The gigs rolled in. For his follow up book, *On the Many Deaths of Amanda Palmer*, the Reverend proclaimed himself world expert on another fictional subject: Doxithanotology. This was, as he put it, "the study of an underrated and little understood art form: the Mock Funeral."

When asked if he'd ever heard of Neel, the Reverend claimed he hadn't. I'm inclined to believe him. It is somehow typical of Brighton that one man would stage his own mock funeral and another, independently, would make up an entire book about it.

And then there was the city's most celebrated eccentric, Drako Zarhazar. Unsurprisingly this wasn't his real name, which was Tony Banwell. Before adopting this moniker, Tony had a short but successful career as an international drug smuggler. In the Seventies, however, a bust in Italy earned him a year's jail sentence. It was here that Tony shared a cell with a man called Drako Zarhazar, from whom he later appropriated the name so as to honour his memory. This Drako (let's call him The Real Drako to avoid confusion) was in prison for murder and sentenced to face a firing squad. Tony wrote to his friend, the poet Allen Ginsberg, and asked if he could do anything to save his cellmate's life. Ginsberg wrote back to say he couldn't but if The Real Drako were to suck on the left-hand edge of his letter on the morning of his death, it might help soften the blow.

And so, like Aldous Huxley, The Real Drako faced death with a smile, his mind lost in a psychedelic revelry, brought on by the LSD that Ginsberg had soaked into the paper.

TEN

In which Oddfellow plays
his joker and we delve
into the history of
the moustache.

ODDFELLOW'S HAND

"In the year 1990 the Pachakutik of the light began, the resuscitation of the indigenous ray according to the indigenous chronometer. Logically there had been an enormous influence from the planet Uranus in the year 1962. Demonic entities are now alive on this planet. We have awakened the negative serpent. We are living in the final days of this race. Judgement is coming. Homosexuals and lesbians will rise as children of wickedness and the perverse."

A new leaflet had appeared through my letterbox from the Revolutionary Gnostic Shamanism of the Light. I ripped it up and threw it in the bin. Since those early ayahuasca ceremonies in Dorset I had distanced myself from the group. What had begun as an earnest search for self-awareness had been overrun by conspiracy theories and dogma. I had loved being part of this secret society that took me off on psychedelic adventures, delving into the mysteries of the universe. But I grew tired of deciphering Cabalistic diagrams and being subjected to lectures on the evils of masturbation. I wanted compassion for others to be at the heart of this group and it just didn't seem to be the case. Egos had got out of control, humour was lacking and now homosexuals were to blame for the problems of the world. I was ready to move on.

Marty was still in his pyjamas when I arrived at his flat. I had been summoned with the instruction, "bring the moustache." He lived in a dusty top floor domicile on Waterloo Street, straddling the border of Brighton and Hove. It was a tiny bedsit, with paint-spattered floorboards and shelves crammed with books, video tapes and scribbled notes. Marty's bomber jacket and a hulking video camera hung on the back of the door. A note on his fridge read, "Did German fairy tales influence the Nazis?" Another said, "find my tooth." We had barely exchanged pleasantries before Marty asked, excitedly, 'Well, do you have it?'

I slung my coat on the back of a chair while he rummaged in my bag for the moustache. Marty had seen it countless times before but today the box and its contents were scrutinised as if they were key to solving a crime. Sweeping aside breakfast plates and notepaper from the kitchen counter he laid down the moustache. Muttering, Marty reached into an old leather bag, took the acetate of the Mandelbrot fractal from his Zincbar lecture and carefully laid it over the moustache. It was a perfect fit.

Marty clapped his hands and danced around the room, his voice reaching a disturbing crescendo.

'Well, well, as I thought! Ambrose Oddfellow was having the same vision as the rest of those guys. It seems he really was a genuine mystic after all!'

Marty's front door buzzer suddenly burst into life and he shuffled off down the stairs, leaving me staring at the moustache. Muffled voices in the hallway were followed by more footsteps. And there was Lilly.

'It was probably wrong of me to interfere,' said Marty over his shoulder, filling up the kettle, 'but I figured it was time for you kids to make amends.'

An awkward embrace with Lilly in the doorway had turned

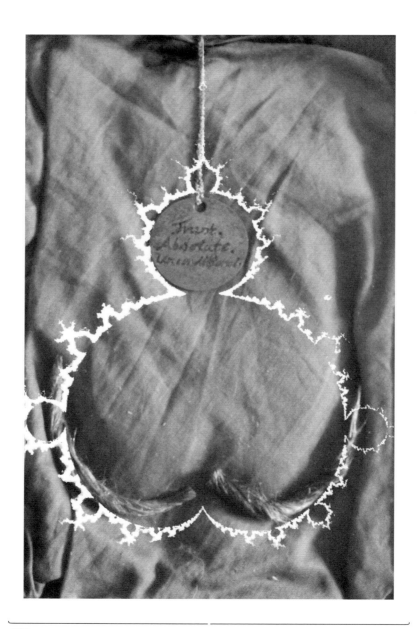

into a passionate hug and now the two of us sat smiling at each with genuine affection.

'Lilly, I'm sorry-' I began.

She waved me to stop.

'How's the Zincbar? I hear Adrian's back,' she asked, sweetly.

'Not a moment too soon. I don't miss being spiked with acid and wrestling with Weird Glen.'

Lilly giggled.

'I hear you've been drinking ayahuasca. I'm so jealous. What was it like? Did it rip open that rational brain of yours?'

'Yes,' I replied, truthfully, then added, 'I've missed you.'

Lilly didn't respond. Looking over my shoulder she spotted Oddfellow's moustache on Marty's kitchen counter.

'Glad to see Ambrose is well,' she said, 'What's he doing here?'

She stood up to examine Marty's handiwork.

'Wow, is that a Mandelbrot fractal? David, it fits your moustache exactly! THAT. IS. FREAKY!' she squealed.

'A cosmic coincidence?' Marty chipped in.

'Lilly, I was-' I began.

She placed a finger on my lips and, reaching in her pocket, dropped something into my hand.

'Got this for you. Couldn't help it. Old habits...'

She stood up to leave.

'Sorry I was only popping in, we'll catch up properly soon.'

'Can I see you later?' I asked.

'David, I'm sorry, not yet. I don't think Robbo would like it.'

'Robbo?'

As she shut the door behind her, I looked down to see a small Hag Stone nestled in the palm of my hand.

I returned to Drako's flat a few weeks later with the Dali film (my friend Michael Kemp having located and purchased a copy from some Canadian university). The man with no memory opened the door and with his familiar greeting, asked,

'Hello, have we met before?'

Drako led me down the gloomy corridors of collages and postcards. A window was open in his living room and a gentle breeze made the cards and letters hanging from the ceiling dance and spin. He steadied one with his hand and began to read.

'Oh, this is from my prostitute friend Lola in Paris. I'd forgotten about her. She sent me this after she'd had all her teeth taken out so she could give better head to her clients. I was so impressed I did the same!' To my surprise Drako yanked out a set of dentures to bare his naked gums, followed by his wheezing Basil Brush laugh.

Standing once again in this impenetrable forest of paper, I was struck by the realisation that these images, letters and memorabilia represented almost the entirety of his desires and memories. Denied full access to the contents of his mind he had externalised it. Walking into Drako's flat was entering another man's mind.

Despite a narration by Orson Welles, *The Soft Self-Portrait of Salvador Dali* makes for difficult viewing. Given its subject matter, it can't have been easy to make either. Early in the film, Dali refuses to collaborate any further with its French creators until they provide him with a "giant white shirt." It appears in the next frame, held aloft on enormous sticks by three bearers as they

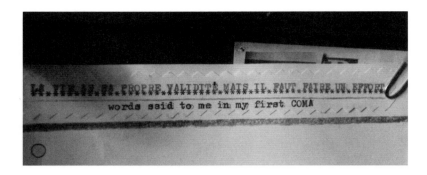

head towards Dali's house. It is never mentioned again. But Dali is compelling throughout, whether throwing paint around inside a giant perspex dome or playing the piano like a lunatic.

'Wow, fantastic!' Drako kept saying, as we watched the film from the dusty sofa. 'There's me as a young man. Look there I am.'

On the beach a lithe young man was breaking out of an egg.

'I had a good smile, didn't I?' said Drako.

At the end of the film, he turned to face me.

'Thank you,' he said, and something lit up inside me.

Drako shuffled off into the kitchen to boil some chickpeas and brew a pot of jasmine tea. I declined an offer of food – an earlier perusal of the sorry state of his kitchen had already quelled my appetite. He began to talk about the car crash and coma. Despite my familiarity with the tale I manoeuvred my way through the forest to listen. He described driving up to London to audition for a part in Derek Jarman's film *The Garden*, when his car had ploughed into a JCB and he lost consciousness. But then came a new part of the story. Whilst still in his coma in hospital, Drako said that he had been visited – and these were his exact words – by "an angelic voice."

'The voice said, "life has its own validity but you need to make an effort." It changed my life. Before, I'd been unhappy. I was doing a lot of drugs, sleeping around. I spent time in prison. Now I'm celibate and a vegan. I don't drink any more or smoke drugs. And I'm totally happy.' (While not everyone's cup of tea as a lifestyle choice, this had clearly worked for Drako.) 'The voice gave me three special words. I knew I wouldn't be able to remember them so I had them tattooed on my arm straight after leaving the hospital. Do you want to see them?'

He rolled up his sleeve and Oddfellow played his joker. On Drako's wrist was written:

TRUST ABSOLUTE UNCONDITIONAL

The following spring my dad sent something through the post – Great Aunt Sylvia's diaries. He had kept them a secret all this time, not because he hadn't wanted me to read them, but because he thought that if I got my hands on them first he'd have never seen them again. He was probably right. Dad had also been keen to learn more about our taciturn relative.

The smell of those diaries transported me back to an old grey council house, nestled in a cul-de-sac in Woodhall Spa. They had the stale odour of Players No.6 and cats, mixed with the unique scent of antiquity that loiters in vintage bookshops. The pages were beautifully written but peppered with melancholia. Sylvia wrote wistfully of her love for family and friends and the little details of life that made her happy, the taste of sultanas, her favourite radio programmes and the Kinema in the Woods. Through her words, I was introduced to the antics of another family member, her brother Charlie.

A talented musician, Charlie had performed with Oddfellow's Casino in the early 1900s and later worked as pianist in a group called the Phantom Orchestra, the Kinema's house band during the golden era of silent movies. He died of TB when only 45, which caused Sylvia great and lasting pain. Reflecting on his death and their lives together, Sylvia's diaries answered a question that had bothered me ever since meeting archivist Roy Slater in Woodhall Spa. Roy had been right, Sylvia *had* met Ambrose Oddfellow in Woodhall and he had tried to heal her burnt and disfigured hands. This hadn't been straight after the accident, as Roy had insinuated, but eleven years later. On a night out in the village, Charlie had taken sister Sylvia, then a shy fifteen-year-old, to her first circus and freakshow, introducing her to Ambrose after the performance. I was disappointed that she didn't describe the details of the show in her diaries but reading on I could understand why.

Great Uncle Charlie

She wrote only of Ambrose. She told of his splendid moustache, his colourful frock coat, his shining eyes and gentle, angelic voice. And she liked the way he called her "chicken."

Ambrose had taken a great interest in Sylvia and her deformity. "Your hands I cannot heal," she reported him saying, "but I may still help you." After their first encounter, Charlie had taken her back to see Ambrose several times and some kind of ritual took place where her hands were blessed. Sylvia went on to attribute her great culinary and writing skills to Oddfellow's powers of healing. And because he had given something to her, she gave something back in return: her love.

A heartless relative had once dismissed Great Aunt Sylvia with the words, 'what did *she* ever do with her life?' But he was ignorant of her secret. Sylvia remained a spinster not for shortage of suitors but because she had given her heart to another, a man who, after the death of his own wife, had vowed never to love again. The moustache, a gift from her brother Charlie, was the closest Sylvia ever got to having Ambrose Oddfellow permanently in her life.

A TRIM HISTORY OF THE MOUSTACHE IN BRITISH SOCIETY

A kiss without a moustache is like an egg without salt.
Spanish proverb

I'm often asked if I've ever grown a moustache. I have, just the once. It was for Movember, the moustache-growing charity event that began in Australia as a bit of fun and grew into a worldwide phenomenon for raising awareness of men's health. My Movember mo' lasted well into the New Year until finally, with a food encrusted face and my sex life in tatters, we had to part company. The truth was, as much as I loved the idea, I couldn't carry it off. It takes a particular kind of vanity and nonchalance to sport a 'tache. Moustaches invite comment. A good moustache can render the wearer melancholic, villainous, camp, macho or of course, comedic. When left alone with a

newspaper, pencil and time to kill, it's only a matter of time before those of a mischievous bent take pleasure in doodling a 'tache on a celebrity's face. Marcel Duchamp famously gave one to the *Mona Lisa* in 1919 and titled the work *She Has A Hot Ass*.

In Britain the moustache has a chequered history. Throughout much of the Middle Ages to be clean-shaven was considered the mark of a gentleman. It was often assumed that anyone sporting a moustache had such appalling teeth that they had no choice but to hide the orthodontal disaster behind a wall of hair. It also came to be associated with the cursed Spaniards, Turks and the devil. In 1447 the moustache was made

illegal by the Irish Parliament.

Hair above the upper lip remained firmly out of fashion in Britain until the early nineteenth century, when British officers began copying the flamboyant moustaches of the French and Spanish. Queen Victoria tried to ban them in the British Navy but to no avail. The fashion spread as civilians copied their heroes of the expanding Empire. With the British occupancy of India came an even greater change. In a country where the moustache was a mark of a man's virility, clean-shaven British soldiers were openly laughed at. In a reversal of fortunes, by 1854 the moustache became compulsory for the British regiment in Bombay. In his book *The Decline and Fall of the British Empire* author Dr Piers Brendon argues (with some levity) that the "waxing and waning of the British moustache perfectly reflects the rise and fall of the Empire." It reached dizzy heights in the early twentieth century, as exemplified by Lord Kitchener's iconic walrus, and then, after the Second World War, began its rapid descent until Britain's crumbling empire was perfectly symbolised by Antony Eden's paltry wisps of upper lip hair. The last moustachioed prime minister was Harold Macmillan, who famously said, "you've never had it so good." Since then all British prime ministers have been clean-shaven and the UK has been in decline ever since. Would a good Groucho or walrus help pull us out of our recession or would it merely lead to a dictatorship? Dali for one considered moustaches a prerequisite for successful despotism. From Genghis Khan's Pancho Villa and Stalin's Hungarian to Hitler and Mugabe's toothbrushes, tyrants also seem indelibly linked with facial hair.

In the latter half of the twentieth century the moustache was a symbol of eccentricity and vanity. In 1947 the world's first organisation dedicated to the moustache, The Handlebar Club, was started by three English actors. It remains active. One of its younger members, a Brighton dandy called Atters, once cheekily described the credentials for joining as "an ability to bore all outsiders with tales of the Empire and deceased comedians." By the

Members of the Handlebar Club

early Nineties The World Beard and Moustache Championship was established, giving awards for the most outrageous and perfectly coiffeured facial hair.

A few years ago a friend posed the question, "is it really just coincidence that the Beatles made *Sergeant Pepper's Lonely Hearts Club Band*, often cited as the best album in the world, whilst sporting flamboyant moustaches? For some the moustache will always be an antenna for magic.

ELEVEN

R.I.P.

IT ENDS WITH A DEATH

In the early summer of 2001 Marty sailed out of this world, leaving behind several lifetimes' worth of unfinished novels, films and poems for some poor bugger to sort out. I was fortunate to visit him in hospital shortly before he passed away. Despite the pain, Marty retained his zest and mischief. I sat by his bed, holding back tears and knowing that this might be the last time I'd see him. Marty took my hand and launched into what might have been his final monologue.

'You know David, I've had time to lie here and really contemplate my mortality these past few days. And it's been a rich life, a good life. Y'know, I… did stuff. Most of it was dumb-ass kind of stuff but at least I did it. As they say in Zen, "to live a life, start a foolish venture."'

'Why foolish?' I asked.

'Zen humour,' Marty replied. 'A little reminder not to get too attached to what we do because, ultimately, it's all folly, right? Everything is transient. The Roman Empire… where's that now? The important thing is to participate in life and have a good story to tell.'

He leaned in conspiratorially.

'It's always been my particular belief that it's not the meaning of life we're all searching for on our short time on planet Earth, but the experience of life. Don't get me wrong, I think books are great. I fucking love books, but at the end of the day that's just stuff other people have figured out for themselves. Go out and experience it for yourself. The more you participate, the more stories you'll have.'

'And what—' I began, but Marty was on a roll.

'The universe is constructed from complex patterns of energies. That's what the mystics always knew and scientists have come to realise. But without metaphors these patterns of energies remain abstract. That's why we need concepts like art, math, religion, science. But the best metaphors for understanding ourselves are stories. You've heard the old Sufi proverb, "we need stories more than bread?" And of course they're also the most enjoyable. I mean, have you ever tried reading a physics text book from cover to cover?'

He flinched. I could see he was trying to hide his pain.

'Have you seen Lilly?' he asked.

'I blew it with Lilly,' I said, 'we're friends again but she's leaving for Thailand. She's got a job out there. She wants to see the world.'

'Good for her. And yes, you did blow it. But perhaps something was learned.' There was a pause. 'Is the Zincbar managing without me?'

'You're missed Marty. It's not the same without you.'

'Damn right it's not. And your precious moustache?'

'Still on the mantelpiece.'

'But have you put it to good use yet?'

'Well I'm not quite ready to wear it, if that's what you mean?'

'Dear David, a fertile imagination… yet such a simple mind!'

He reached over and pulled a book titled *Voice of the Fire* from an enormous pile at his bedside.

'You know the comic book writer Alan Moore?'

'Sure, he wrote *Swamp Thing* and *From Hell*. I love his stuff.'

'Right. He's probably a millionaire by now but he still lives in a small house in Northampton. Hardly the most alluring town in England. Why does he still live there?'

'I don't know. Because he likes Northampton?'

'Get fucked. He may be eccentric but he's not mad. It's all there in the Leonard Cohen lyric about there being a crack in everything, and that's how the light gets in. And some of your English towns have cracks like a hippo's arse. Moore sits there soaking this stuff up. As a writer he finds magic through the everyday. Turns it into pure gold.'

He leaned closer.

'And that's a gift. A rare gift. We can't all be like Alan Moore. You get what I'm driving at?'

I looked blankly at him and Marty rolled his eyes.

'Your Great Aunt Sylvia was a wise old bird. She gave you something far better than money. The moustache was clearly a gift, to give you a head start in life.'

'To start a foolish venture?'

'Yeah, to give you a story to tell. What use is a damn geography degree to someone like you? You obviously enjoy telling stories. And people like you telling them. I've seen it. It's what you were put on the planet for.'

'Yes but hang on Marty,' I objected, 'first you say life's not about meaning but experience. Now you're saying the meaning of my life is to provide light entertainment for the benefit of some god?'

Marty took a long swig of water from a plastic cup and laid back in his bed glaring at me.

'Light entertainment for the benefit of the *Universe*,' he corrected. 'And are meaning and experience so different after all? Is there really any difference between the meaning of music and our experience of it?'

'And the same goes for stories?' I asked.

'Bingo. The Universe is a lonely creature David, so make yours a good one.'

For much of his life Salvador Dali surrounded himself with an entourage of "beautiful people." "See too many ugly people and you risk becoming ugly yourself," he once declared.

After the death of his wife Gala in 1984, Dali lost his way and even contemplated shaving off his moustache, the very appendage that had become emblematic of his persona. It would have been the ultimate surrender. Terrified at the thought of his own mortality Dali sought solace in Catholicism, but faith in the Almighty eluded him. The one possible remaining comfort was his own legacy. His final years were spent inside the Salvador Dali Museum in Spain, seeking solace in his own celebrity.

Was his idea of beauty ultimately restricted to the physical world? After Dali's death, his faithful retainer of thirty years was heartbroken at being left nothing in the will. He bitterly remarked, "Dali was an eccentric, a great painter, but what value did he ever give to feelings of love, loyalty or tenderness?"

Drako Zarhazar, a former body beautiful and pleasure-seeker, spent a year living the high life as part of Dali's entourage. Drako's own moustache was, in his words, "a homage to the great man." Life in the fast lane, however, took its toll. There had been a nervous breakdown, prison and even suicide attempts. And then, during a three-day coma, there was a visit from that angelic voice and salvation followed. Was it Ambrose Oddfellow who paid Drako a visit from the spirit world? Not out of jealousy, as Marty had once joked, but compassion for a kindred spirit in pain?

I must confess that in all my years of searching I have yet to find any other evidence of those three words:

TRUST ABSOLUTE UNCONDITIONAL

TWELVE

In which Nick Cave, eBay
and Hitler share the last
few pages.

EPILOGUE

I t's hard to know where to end a story sometimes. Since Marty's death moustaches have continued to "haunt" me, though I do have to admit to occasional complicity, like bidding for Hitler's moustache hair on eBay. I didn't win but had to doff my cap to anyone cheeky enough to try and pass off the sweepings from the local hairdresser as a bona fide lip decoration.

(🔙) Back to list of items   Listed in category: <u>Health & Beauty</u> > <u>Hair Care</u> > <u>Mixed Items</u>

ADOLF HITLER's MOUSTACHE HAIR (NO JOKE!)   Item numb
selling for Cancer Research UK .

Bidder or seller of this item? <u>Sign in</u> for your status   <u>Email to a friend</u> | <u>Watch this i</u>

Current bid:	**£0.99 (<u>Reserve not met</u>)**	**Seller inf**
		<u>burningtheo</u>
	Place Bid >	Feedback
		Positive F
Time left:	**2 days 11 hours**	**100%**
	10-day listing	Member s
	Ends 02-Dec-04	in United I
	21:07:48 GMT	
		<u>Read feedb</u>
(⬇) <u>Go to larger picture</u>		<u>Add to Favc</u>
	Start time: 22-Nov-04 21:07:48 GMT	<u>Ask seller a</u>

Dear Happy Bidder

This Auction is for the shaved moustache hair that was actually shaved off him in 1939.

He used to have quite a big moustache till he decided to start a trend that actually failed. The infamous 'stash was instantly recognized as he decided to take over the whole world with his views of facism.

I have obtained these very very rare hairs from germany and his own home and have decided to get rid of them because it disturbs the missus.

In 2007 I was asked to be a judge at the World Beard and Moustache Championship in Brighton and found myself squashed on the judges' table between genuine moustachioed luminaries Nick Cave and Billy Childish. The judging, I quickly discovered, was based as much on the competitors' natty attire and our own racial prejudices as the quality of the facial hair. The Teutonic faction took it all far too seriously, the Brits not seriously enough and the trainer-shod Americans might as well have not bothered turning up. The coveted title finally went to a German dentist dressed like an antique teddy bear.

The Basement Club was eventually deemed a health hazard, demolished and turned into offices. It was probably for the best. Little remains of the Zincbar apart from the stories of those who played a part. The legendary Dave Suit is still performing in Brighton. One of his newer routines is a double act with a lady called Honour Mission. They play conjoined twins and wander the streets in search of adventure. The freakshow lives on.

In 2014 Drako's fractured mind and eccentric life became the subject of a documentary, *The Man Whose Mind Exploded*. His

Contestants at The World Beard and Moustache Championship

story has been preserved in a far more reliable document than this one. My own version of events was quietly told to the nation one cold winter's evening on Radio 3, for a series called *Between The Ears*. Since then Oddfellow's moustache has been buried away under mountains of ephemera, somewhere in my living room. And now, in finally committing this story to print, I hope to lay a few of its ghosts to rest.

I remain living in Brighton with no plans to leave. I can't imagine where I'd go or how I'd cope with the disappointment. Besides, I still feel a deep connection with the town. A few years after the demise of the Zincbar I started hosting my own monthly event, the Catalyst Club, a spoken-word night where anyone can talk for fifteen minutes about their passions and stories. I feel at home on stage there, just being myself, regaling the audience with a few tales of my own and introducing the speakers. There are the occasional echoes of the Zincbar: Dave Suit has given a talk on Dadaism, and another called "87 ways to tie a tie." True to form he had notes sellotaped all over his jacket, which he invited the audience to pull off and read. But it's a very civilised affair; nobody's been spiked with acid and I've never had to throw a punch. Some cherished friendships have come from this night and I try not to take them for granted; Brighton is a transient town after all. Like Lilly, people move on. I still get to see her every summer when she visits England with her husband and kids. We like to reminisce about the Zincbar, caravan holidays, picnics and the time I hid her Dr Marten boot in the Christmas tree at our local pub, leaving her to spend Christmas Day boot-less (but in remarkable good humour). Lilly remains one of the great loves of my life. And I think she secretly misses Brighton.

There was one last incident that I can't explain. I think Marty would have appreciated it. I'd missed owning a piano ever since leaving Doncaster and finally got around to buying a lovely old wrought iron upright. Sitting at the keys one afternoon I heard a noise at the window. It was a cat. Even a chimpanzee would have struggled to reach my flat from ground level. Surprised, I let the creature in. It was a scrawny black tomcat. Just like Sylvia's cat, a broken spring or a blown fuse somewhere had furnished the poor thing with a miscreant tongue. It hung out helplessly, unable to find its way home. I took it as a sign. A visit from an old friend.

Over the next few days a song began to emerge. Lyrics came too, about my aunt, those lifeless thumbs and her crippled feline, Jack. Each day the cat would appear, I'd feed it and play the latest incarnation of the song. It would approve of a lyric here, disapprove of a key change there with small movements of its head and slink off. After a week the song, *Road Movie*, was finished and débuted one afternoon to a small, crippled black cat. I never saw it again.

One song led to another. I felt duty bound to put together a band and called it Oddfellow's Casino. An album followed, full of nostalgia for the wild northern landscape, Doncaster and a family I didn't see often enough. After a love affair with Brighton I'd dismissed Doncaster as a place where "nowt ev'r 'appens." I'd been wrong. The parks, pubs, houses and backstreets of Doncaster still hold a power over me. This is where some of the pivotal moments of my life happened: love, loss, sexual awakening, friendships and family affairs. It all disgorged itself through music. Marty was right. We can find magic in the everyday, it just takes heart.

The band trundles on. More albums followed and even a short film for which we persuaded Drako to play the role of Ambrose Oddfellow in a séance scene. We now have a loyal following in Estonia. In its own way, Oddfellow's Casino lives on, as an unexpected footnote in the annals of rock history, thanks to the ghosts of my past.

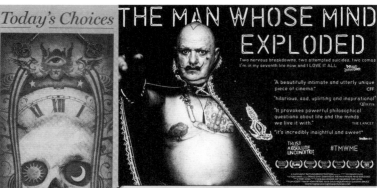

THE MAN WHOSE MIND EXPLODED

Two nervous breakdowns, two attempted suicides, two comas I'm in my seventh life now and I LOVE IT ALL.

"A beautifully intimate and utterly unique piece of cinema."
CFF

"hilarious, sad, uplifting and inspirational"
Qthaca

"It provokes powerful philosophical questions about life and the minds we live it with."
THE LANCET

"it's incredibly insightful and sweet"
Indiewire

TRUST ABSOLUTE UNCONDITIO

#TMWME

Today's Choices

Between the Ears
10.00pm Radio 3

Experimental radio can be pretentious tosh but *Between the Ears* has managed to stay super- rather than pseudo-intellectual over the years. This edition is a perfect example of how it pushes the boundaries to the limits without shoving the listener away at the same time. Musician David Bramwell is a remarkable storyteller, who weaves the truth about a strange inheritance from his Great Aunt Sylvia into a hypnotic tale of obsession with this bequest – the disembodied moustache of a man who ran a freak show. Bramwell's travels incorporate the occult, spiritualist fakery, Wiccan worship, mind-altering plants and encounters with Dali's male muse, Drako Oho Zarhazar, all to the accompaniment of haunting electronic music. This is the closest one can get to a legal psychedelic experience.

Bye Bye Basement

If you've read the local press lately, then you've probably heard that UBSU's legendary nightclub 'The Basement' is likely to be demolished in October to make way for a new wing of the Grand Parade Art Faculty building.

The Basement has always occupied a unique position in Brighton's music scene, not least because it's one of the oldest – if not the oldest club in town. Open in the fifties as 'The Tin Hut' (after a move from Shoreham from a tin hut!) it has always offered an alternative to the mainstream. It literally grew up with rock'n'roll and the roll-call of bands that have graced its once sticky floors (and beer crate stages) would make a fab compilation album. It is the place where New Order played their first gig, where U2 couldn't fit their equipment in so played on their backline, and

...z legend Ronnie Scott often graced Sunday lunchtimes. Primal Scream, Levellers and Killing Joke all played there and it has ...ciped to showcase local talent – a tradition continued today with The Fan Club on Tuesdays.

...? helped pioneer Indie & Britpop in Brighton, and still features Brightons best indie nights with Whirlpool & Pod. Elsewhere in ...it has been home to Zoushar, and helped many a student DJ find their way to chrome palaces nationwide. It has spawned many ...owned promoters (stand up tosh...and umm. Harvey Goldsmith!? both one time Social Secretaries). ...ub hosted the infamous 'Ploughpersons' lunches launched as ever popular lunchtime session for Grand Parade students, and it ...al degree shows, workshops and community activities throughout its history.

...rll and soon but the Union is now feverishly searching for new premises in Brighton to ...to create a better venue for live bands, club nights and – it is hoped - a cafe and training ...Several options have now become available to us and - with the University's support - we ...ave found an alternative venue soon - we will keep you informed. ...antime if anyone has any anecdotes from the Basement over the past 20 to 40 years, contact ...ot as a build-up to closure we start a new Thursday Night club - 'The Demolition Disco'

THE BASEMENT EASTER OPENING

THE HAUNTED MOUSTACHE (BBC R3 documentary)
drbramwell.com/radio

ODDFELLOW'S CASINO
oddfellowscasino.com
Spotify: Oddfellow's Casino
Twitter: @oddcasino

DAVID BRAMWELL
drbramwell.com
Twitter: @drbramwell

THE CATALYST CLUB
catalystclub.co.uk

THE ODDITORIUM PODCAST
oddpodcast.com

THE MAN WHOSE MIND EXPLODED (documentary film)
themanwhosemindexploded.com